One-Way Ticket

by

MARGARET WAY

P9-DMM-622

Harlequin Books

TORONTO • LONDON • NEW YORK • AMSTERDAM • SYDNEY

Original hardcover edition published in 1977
by Mills & Boon Limited

ISBN 0-373-02111-9

Harlequin edition published October 1977

Printed in U.S.A.

Harlequin

is pleased to announce the forthcoming release of its first motion picture, based on the best-selling novel by Anne Mather

Harlequin Presents...

KEIR DULLEA · SUSAN PENHALIGON

Leopard in the Snow

Guest Stars
KENNETH MORE · BILLIE WHITELAW

featuring GORDON THOMSON as MICHAEL
and **JEREMY KEMP** as BOLT

Produced by JOHN QUESTED and CHRIS HARROP
Screenplay by ANNE MATHER and JILL HYEM
Directed by GERRY O'HARA

An Anglo-Canadian Co-Production

OTHER
Harlequin Romances
by MARGARET WAY

Many of these titles are available at your local bookseller
or through the Harlequin Reader Service.

For a free catalogue listing all available Harlequin Romances,
send your name and address to:

HARLEQUIN READER SERVICE,
M.P.O. Box 707, Niagara Falls, N.Y. 14302
Canadian address: Stratford, Ontario, Canada N5A 6W4

or use order coupon at back of books.

CHAPTER ONE

JAY lit a cigarette and pushed a list of figures back across the wide desk to his brother. 'Looks all right!'

'It *is* right,' Dave muttered without lifting his head.

Jay frowned and tilted his chair off balance. 'You can't go on like this, Dave,' he said pretty grimly. 'For one thing, I'm sick of it and I want a bit of time to myself. To come right down to it, you haven't been worth a bumper since you came back from England. If this girl means so much to you, get her out here. Send her a plane ticket.'

'Using your money?' Dave looked up, startled, the habitual sparkle of friction dying out of his eyes.

'Our money, what's the difference?' Jay asked shortly, bone tired.

Dave glanced at him and smiled, his blue eyes alight with amused malice. 'Never let it be said you're not the cattle baron, brother. No one takes any notice of me. I'm just MacCallister's brother.'

'You could probably fix it to be somebody yourself.'

'No way!' Dave protested with all the old bitterness. '*You're* MacCallister. I'm just one of the hired hands. There can never be any true equality with you, Jay. You're turning yourself into another legend like Dad. You look like him. You even talk like him and from a distance I could almost swear it was him in the saddle. There's no excuse for you, Jason MacCallister the third!'

'Okay, boy, let's move off that.'

'There you are!' Dave said in a dazed furious voice.

His brother suddenly slapped the palm of his hand down on the desk. 'Want my job?' His grey eyes illuminated his darkening countenance. He looked formidable, even dangerous, sick to death of ploughing his way through Dave's accumulated resentments, mostly self-inflicted. He could do with someone to shoulder a few of the burdens instead of listening to Dave's perpetual whining.

Almost immediately Dave backed down, starting to smile. '*Me?*'

'No,' Jay said suddenly. 'You just like bucking. Either you're going to be a rogue, Dave, or you're going to get down to working out your own destiny. All this running friction is tedious. You're too old for it.'

'Twenty-seven?' Dave asked, flicking paper-clips around erratically. 'I'm not ready to retire.'

'Stop that!' Jay ordered, and knocked his brother's hand away. 'Surely it's sunk in that Greg has been doing your job long enough.'

'Greg is content to hero-worship Big Brother. I'm different!'

'Don't gloat over it. It's a big drawback.'

'All right, all right!' Dave said at once in the helpless kind of voice that always lessened Jay's anger and made him draw on fresh patience.

'What in the name of God do you want?' Jay asked, his tone easing up to an almost sympathetic request. 'This girl—what's her name? I should remember but I don't!'

'Melanie.'

6

'God damn it!' Jay murmured, amused.

'It suits her!' Dave glanced up hotly. 'She's beautiful. Small and elegant. She'll be unique out here with her white skin and her silver ribbon of hair.'

'Great! Just what we need, in fact, a piece of porcelain. What's her other name? It's got to be an improvement on Melanie.'

'Melanie Kent.'

'Remarkable. What does she do?'

'She's an illustrator for children's stories.'

'Stop there,' Jay interrupted. 'This girl is outside my experience. I'm fairly ignorant on that score.'

'Meet her, Jay. You'll love her, but she'll never love you. She's too gentle.'

'And I'm some kind of a tyrant?'

'You're tough. Hard at times!' Dave looked across the table at his brother's dark, self-sufficient face. Jay had nothing to do to impress people. He looked what he was, and he probably wasn't even aware of his own image, an image their dead father had bequeathed to him, excluding Dave and their youngest brother, Greg. Directly above and behind Jay's crisp black head was the big portrait of their father that Dave never looked at if he could help it. It showed a handsome, dynamic man in his late forties, a strong, positive man who worked desperately hard and saw a vision of the land with his striking light eyes. It was a portrait Dave couldn't cope with and he always turned his back on it. The day would come when Jay would look just like that, and a curious love-hate smouldered in him like a glowing fire. Even if he *had* been the eldest brother he would never have stood a chance against Jay. Their father had

7

idolised Jay, giving every outward appearance of treating all three of his sons the same. Their sister, Susan, he had spoiled outrageously, but she was only a girl and she never came into his plans beyond fixing her up nicely when she got married. Their mother had died when Sue was born, for no good reason at all, and Dave could still feel the taste of the sickness and grief in his mouth. He had never got over his frustrated agony at not having the mother who had understood him best of all. Melanie with her hair like silk and her intensely green eyes bore a superficial resemblance. She made him feel confident, a man with no problem, not some second-rate shadow of Jay.

'You're serious, then?' Jay asked, unwilling to sit around any longer.

'Just as serious as I'll ever be.'

'And the ravishing Melanie?'

'The letters have been flying back and forth. You don't miss anything. I'll bet you know every line of her writing.'

'That's your kind of game,' Jay said, stretching his arms. 'God, I'm tired! I could weep into a cold beer. Why any man bothers to fall in love I don't know, but it seems you have.'

'That's putting it mildly,' said Dave.

'What about Hilary?'

'I don't have to explain myself to Hilary!' Dave pulled a sour face. 'It's Melanie I want. All I ever do is think about her.'

'Right. Which gives me the idea. Send her an open ticket and she can fly out any time she likes. If she's as serious as you're making out, she won't lose any time.

I suppose you filled her in with a few details.'

'Meaning what?'

'Meaning, brother, most women are interested in a little financial betterment. You'd be a fool to expect anything else.'

Dave's good-looking face was becoming flushed. 'Listen here, Jay, just because women hurl themselves at you . . .'

'It's the name, boy,' Jay interrupted. 'We've got one.'

'That sounds like an echo of Dad,' said Dave bitterly.

'Then I won't further the recitation. I take it, however, sweet Melanie knows what line we're in?'

'Do you mean did I tell her about the chain?'

'Got it.' Jay's light grey eyes shimmered.

'That among other things!' said Dave, directing his attention back to the paper-clips.

'Then she'll come!' Jay predicted, easing his lean, hard body. 'If nothing else she should have a pleasant trip.'

Dave glared back at him. 'Let me tell you Melanie's no ordinary girl. She's intelligent and creative, and best of all she's not even aware of the great Jason Mac-Callister's existence.'

'How careless! She'll have to know some time.'

Dave shrugged. His clenched fist opened and dropped aimlessly to his side. 'Do you mean this, Jay?'

'I'm sorry you have to ask that, Dave? Would I have suggested it if I didn't mean it? I honestly try not to waste time. What about her family?'

'Forget them. She works in London. Her father, I understand, is kind and considerate, but he remarried some time ago and the new Mrs Kent sounds like a jealous bitch. Melanie rarely goes home.'

'So she's unhappy?'

'I didn't say that.'

'It stands to reason. An unpleasant episode in her life. How old is she? I've got to learn a lot quickly. Up until now I haven't been taking this current rave too seriously.'

Dave twisted his head up. 'I love her.'

'I hope you mean it. This is going to be a one-way ticket!'

'I'll marry her.'

'It might settle you at that!'

'You think I've failed you, don't you, Jay?' sighed Dave. 'Dad believed the same.'

Jay compressed his shapely mouth. 'God, Dave, you over-dramatise yourself, the Lord knows why! I've done my utmost to help you. Dad even went so far as to indulge you.'

'None of us meant anything to him with you around.'

Jay stared at him, disliking all of this intensely. 'This is your own hang-up, Dave. Sue and Greg feel no such thing. Stop thinking along these lines. It's unhealthy. Surely being a MacCallister provides some compensations, the trips around the world?'

Dave gave a short, harsh laugh. 'At least I met Melanie.'

'And you took her to all the best places and I bet regaled her with a few expensive gifts.'

'You're such a cynic, Jay.'

'I know women,' Jay said dryly.

'That you do. Why don't you marry one?'

'No harm in taking my time. No harm at all.'

Dave risked an opinion. 'Nothing really means anything to you outside of Coorrabin.'

'Coolong, Coraki, Coulta Creek. Don't forget the rest of them, and don't forget, brother, I work like a dog!'

Knowing this was true, Dave felt a momentary wave of self-disgust. Jay always did get personally involved in his problems, though Dave frequently savagely denied it. It was Jay's job, of course, to run things, on his wide shoulders fell all the burdens, so when he spoke it was well worth the effort to listen. 'Can I fix up about the ticket in the morning?' he asked.

'Let me know how much it costs these days and I'll write out the cheque. First class, of course, as befitting a future MacCallister bride.'

'I'd like to send her something a bit more substantial than just a ticket—you know, to reassure her,' Dave added.

'Wouldn't you insult her?' Jay asked in a clipped voice, his dark face sardonic.

'She hasn't got much money.'

'Really? At the very least I imagined she could clothe herself—or maybe she's worth remembering without them!'

Dave's swift anger jetted. He jumped to his feet, but Jay was there before him, smiling with the living charm he had no right to. 'Sorry! I withdraw that. Any girl with a name like Melanie would value her chastity.'

'As a matter of fact she does!' snapped Dave.

'Such girls usually induce a reckless urgency.'

'Oh, shut up, Jay! I wanted her, I'll admit, but I had to forget about it.'

11

'Then let's get this perfect girl out to Coorrabin. You've kindled even my imagination.'

'Don't take her off me, Jay,' Dave said in a voice his brother recognised. 'You'll gain nothing but my undying hatred!'

'You were ready to hate me, Dave, from the day you were born. But just you remember I have no quarrel with you and I want no woman of yours. Your little Melanie is safe. I'll even set you up on Coraki. Think of it as a wedding present!'

A glinting excitement came into Dave's blue eyes. 'No damn fear, you don't mean it!'

'*Make* me appreciate you, Dave. The chain concerns you as much as it concerns me. It's our life, our great-grandfather's dream a reality.'

'You're in charge!' shrugged Dave.

'Don't goad me, Dave. I fit the job much as you regret it. Observe the rules and you'll have a good life. Who needs these domestic conflicts? If you must quarrel, save it for Melanie on Coraki. Think of all the making up!'

'Mind your own business!'

'Coraki *is* my business!' Jay said, suddenly hard. 'Do you want my help or don't you?'

'In three years' time I come into my own money!' said Dave, his handsome face brooding, a weakness about it if one actively looked for it.

Jay saw it, but not with satisfaction. 'I'll give you all the money you want now, with no bother.'

'Money is always useful!' Dave suddenly smiled, his fine teeth, like his brother's, white and dazzling. The family resemblance was there, but it couldn't cover the

12

difference between them. Jay had his every order filled instantly, a natural leader, hard-working and super-efficient. Dave had a bent to his nature that made him his own worst enemy, susceptible to a feeling of inferiority when compared with his elder brother, leading in turn to a kind of arrogance and prickly discontent that every man woman and child on Coorrabin was aware of. Dave was in no sense a relaxing person and he was used to having his own way. He wanted Melanie, and if Jay put it within his reach to get her so much the better. The very thought of her filled him with a taut pain of longing.

Jay just stood there staring at him, his strange light eyes almost raying through him, so sure of himself with their father's unmistakable air of authority. Still, Jay's approval was essential.

'I have to fly out in the morning,' he said now. 'If you're decided on this, Dave, contact Quantas and Coorrabin will pick up the bill. I can see you'll be no good at all until she gets here. You've been in love before.'

'This is different,' Dave stressed.

'Marriage calls for a little reflection,' his brother pointed out.

'You haven't seen Melanie.'

'At least I've been warned. All we can do now is wait and see.'

'Melanie loves me,' Dave maintained, his hand closing over the edge of the desk as though it was the curve of a delicate shoulder.

'That's all right, then!' Jay moved to the door and the light fell across his head throwing into relief the

13

strong bones of his face, his darkly tanned skin, and his luminous grey eyes. He was very light-footed for a man an inch or so over six feet and even Dave could see he would be strikingly attractive to women. His blue glance rested on his brother a trifle grimly.

'Just remember Melanie is my property,' he growled.

'No woman is property! Not these days.'

'You know what I mean, Jay.'

Jay's winged black brows lifted a fraction. 'It may seem to you, Dave, we're always in competition, but I assure you we're not. I wouldn't harm a feather of your little chick. I don't know about Greg, though, if she's as pretty as you say.'

Dave relaxed slightly. 'Greg's not you!'

'We'll have to find a good wife for him as well!' Jay hesitated for a moment, looking back over his shoulder, very tall, easy arrogant, a man in a man's country. His *own* country. 'Melanie, does she ride?'

'Yes, she does.'

'Marvellous. You have a few jobs to catch up on, so you can show her the property at your leisure.'

'I can't wait,' Dave said briefly, an odd vulnerability in every taut line of him.

Jay's eyes were suddenly compassionate. There was always the chance that Dave's little Melanie might find Coorrabin and Dave on his home ground too much for her. In a way he was seeking to manipulate a possible marriage, but somewhere on the periphery of his mind he was conscious that he might have to protect this gentle English girl. What did she really know about Dave? Of the futile battles he pitched and the driving demon that sometimes got in him. It would have been

14

impossible for her to know Dave from a few short months in London. Coorrabin might open her eyes. On the other hand, if she returned Dave's love she might make him. Dave desperately needed someone, so why did it occur to him that they might be playing with fire?

CHAPTER TWO

SYBIL got up to make coffee and Nigel Kent turned to his daughter with something like relief. Dinner had been endless. It was upsetting, the constraint between his wife and his daughter, but it was there and it would not go away. In many ways he felt a sort of traitor to his own daughter, and tonight more than ever with Melanie's momentous news.

'It's such a big decision, darling,' he said, feeling it all deeply. 'Did you have to keep it so secret?'

Melanie took a few seconds to answer even though she knew Sybil would hurry back to join them as soon as she could, which would make everything more difficult. 'Is it because he's an Australian, Father?'

'God bless me, *no*!' her father said, startled. 'What a question! I think one could say Australians are entirely respectable. But it's so far away and you're my only daughter. It's not as though you'll be able to come down and see me. I love you, Melanie, you know that. I'll miss you dreadfully, miss the grandchildren I might have.'

'It may not work out,' Melanie said briefly.

'If you contemplate going at all, you must care a good deal, but damn it all, I can pay your fare!'

'David has plenty of money,' she said patiently. 'I can't afford it and I don't see why you should have to pay for me, Father. Sybil would have something to say about it. I can't stay late. By any standards it's been a full day.'

'A great pity about you and Sybil!' her father sighed heavily.

'It's not unusual nor even unnatural,' Melanie said a little formally. 'Sybil wants you to herself. Perhaps I remind her too much of Mother.'

'You certainly remind *me*!' Nigel Kent screwed up his eyes in concentration. 'Such a blessing you took after Nicole. You could have looked like me.'

'You're a very attractive man, Father,' she smiled.

'For a wonder a few women have thought so, but my little Nicole was fantastically pretty. I can't pretend I'm happy, darling. I liked your David. He has excellent manners, he's good-looking and well off and the rest of it, but is he a first-rate person? Is he going to cherish you, make you happy?'

'I think so!' Melanie said gravely.

'I hope so, darling. I want the best for you. You didn't really have time to get to know him. One must see a man involved in his every day life. You've only seen one side of him, the pleasant side, the nights out and the tripping around. He's charming, I grant you, but you don't know him in all his dimensions.'

'That's why I'm going, Father!' Melanie said, and took her father's hand and patted it.

'Hang Sybil, I'll pay your fare!' Nigel Kent said almost violently. 'I don't want you committing yourself to such a degree.'

'And I don't want any more dissention in this family. I told you, David is extremely well off and I'm almost sure of him. You see, I've never met anyone like him before. I don't expect to again. He's different. I expect it's his background. Besides, Father, and this is very important to me, he *needs* me, really needs me—even you sensed that. I spent hours and hours with him. He cares about me deeply and he has a very infectious charm. I don't know exactly what love's supposed to be, but I know I care enough about David to want to find out.'

Her father frowned as though a tiny splinter of doubt entered his head. 'There's something there, darling,' he said darkly. 'Some faintly uneasy impression I gained.'

'He's not a saint!' Melanie protested.

'He could have a devil in him. Ever consider that?'

'I'm almost sure I love him!' said Melanie, sounding a bit desperate.

'Almost?' her father queried.

'I can't be completely sure until I go there. He's told me a great deal about his property, Coorrabin. It sounds like a small kingdom. Apart from leaving you I'm looking forward to the trip immensely. I wish you could be more happy about it.'

'I can see its more exciting aspects, however,' Nigel Kent admitted. 'Just don't lose yourself in all that vastness. I can't see you at all in a sunbaked outback. Your beautiful skin! You'll have to protect it. Wear a hat at all times. I believe the rate of skin cancer is very high.'

'I'll take precautions, Father, don't worry.'

'I can't help worrying now that I see you're set on it,' her father said candidly. 'Are you sure my marrying again hasn't affected your decision? It would weigh heavily on my conscience if I thought so. Why women can't get on together I'll never know!'

'I can't believe the fault was all mine,' said Melanie. 'Sybil has always considered my presence an intrusion. There's no room for me in her world.'

'Perhaps she's frightened, dear. I know you find her attitude irritating and upsetting, but do you realise some women are lamentably jealous and insecure? It's not as though you're some plain little mouse of a thing. You're beautiful and you're clever. Sybil is just plain scared of you, and she tries to hide it with a form of aggression.'

'You've decided that for yourself,' Melanie said, her green eyes glinting. 'Anyway, Sybil doesn't bother me any more, not like she used to, and I know she looks after you well. There'll be no domestic problems when I'm not around.'

Nigel Kent exclaimed under his breath, confused and saddened by what was happening, his mind re-living for a few seconds the perfect peace of his first marriage. He felt suddenly tired, drained of all energy, seeing the faint look of pity in his daughter's eyes. He ran a hand through her beautiful hair, pushing it off her brow. 'If you go away, Melanie, nothing else seems worth while.'

'*Don't* say that!' Melanie cried swiftly. 'Things will be easier for you and Sybil. I was always the major

18

distraction. Besides, I'll write you reams and it will make you feel easier.'

'My head aches!' her father said, his rugged dark face appearing momentarily much older.

'Believe me, it's for the best, darling.'

'I suppose parents must accept these things. Their children going off to the ends of the earth.'

'No journey's too far these days, you know that. If I stay in Australia I'll make sure you get a trip over.'

Her father smiled wryly. 'At the moment I can't say I enjoy the prospect. I'd much rather you stay here in England. It's just struck me what the loss of the sight of you is going to do to me. Are you sure David's looks and money aren't dazzling you?'

'He wasn't my first admirer,' Melanie pointed out gently, 'neither was he the first to ask me to marry him. My boss did that.'

'Good grief!' exclaimed her father.

'I never told you because it wasn't a serious consideration—I never even realised he thought of me that way,' Melanie explained. 'I wouldn't be too much troubled what David did. I only know he wants to take me on as his equal life's partner.'

Her father's mouth tightened with new speculations. 'Life might not be too easy with him,' he warned.

'Life isn't easy,' Melanie sighed. 'I've never found it so, not since Mother died.'

'My poor little Melanie!'

'Stop brooding, Father!' Melanie said gently. 'When I go to Australia, I'll learn everything there is to know about David. Believe me, it was no passing phase for either of us. My memory of him is very vivid.'

There was a faintly sardonic edge in Nigel Kent's deep voice. 'He's only been gone five or six months.'

'It seems longer!' Melanie said, almost with surprise.

'What about your work?' he asked.

'I can work anywhere, Father. I expect to gain a lot from all my new experiences. David's letters are lonely.'

'You're lonely too.'

'Aren't we all? What does Sybil say, I'm too stand-offish?'

Her father frowned. 'You have a very delicate reserve that I for one very much like, and so do a lot of men.'

Melanie's green eyes looked dreamy. 'Somehow I know Coorrabin is my future.'

'*David*, you mean.'

'Yes. Didn't I say that?'

'No. What about his family?'

'He didn't mention them much. His mother died when he was a child—I gather he adored her. His father died a few years ago, one of those very domineering types, a rugged individualist. I think he almost engulfed David in the way very strong, perhaps ruthless, men do.'

Nigel's eyes were guarded. 'As a breadwinner on a very grand scale one would hardly expect a useless passive type. It would take a very special kind of man to run these vast properties, I should think.'

Melanie pressed back against the sofa, her shoulder touching her father's. 'He robbed David of confidence.'

'What?' A little impatiently her father turned on her. 'A real man, my darling, can be anything he likes. I sensed a tenseness in the boy as though he's not used to

20

playing the significant role. Who runs the station now?'

'Why, David and his staff.'

'Who ran it while he was over here?' he asked.

'I don't really know. What difference does it make?'

'If I'd only realised this would become so serious I'd have taken a great deal more notice of your David. I'm vitally interested in your future.' Involuntarily Nigel's hand jerked out and he turned his daughter's face towards him. Her beauty and dearness was hurting him. He couldn't at that moment imagine life without her somewhere close at hand. 'Melanie——' he stopped, trying to find the right words. The thought of Sybil in the kitchen was hampering him. Had Nicole lived Melanie wouldn't be running off to Australia as she was doing now. Nicole would have filled the house with Melanie's young friends and suitable young men. Sybil's undeniable jealousy now suddenly chilled him. Sybil had done her level best to drive Melanie out of the house—not in any obvious glaring way, at least when he was around. Most women had a jealous streak, and apart from that Sybil was a good wife— never Nicole, but on their own they suited well. It was all so painful and perhaps unavoidable. Melanie had had to accept it when he married Sybil; now he would have to accept her desire to go to her David.

'I'm convinced we can make a go of it, Father,' said Melanie, her voice soft.

'Ah well, then, there's nothing more to be said. Go with my blessing, but the minute you want to come home, you must let me know.'

'That's a promise!' Melanie smiled at her father, but her eyes filled with tears. It was taking a certain kind of courage to get herself out to Australia. She would miss her father dreadfully, but she had really lost him the day he married Sybil; she was more gifted than her father ever suspected at communicating her violent dislike.

Sybil, in the kitchen, unlike her husband, was elated by Melanie's news. It was like winning the lottery, and so unexpected! She had always felt threatened by Nicole's daughter. It was like having Nicole's ghost hanging over her shoulder. Melanie couldn't have picked on a better place than Australia, the opposite end of the earth. For once, Sybil had been pleased to allow Nigel a little quiet conversation with his daughter, delaying the serving of the coffee until she could stand it no longer. She was an excellent cook, dinner had been perfect, and Nigel's favourite chocolate cake would complement the coffee. Perhaps she would have to endure Melanie's presence another hour, then never again. The very thought made her heart swell with new hopes for her marriage and she entered the living room smiling, pushing the dinner trolley before her.

'Here, my dears! If I was a little slow it was deliberate. Nigel, your favourite gateau, the very finest ingredients. Melanie, you're so slim you can manage a large slice. I don't think I told you how lovely you look tonight. Being in love suits you. I knew the moment I set eyes on David he would be the one!'

Melanie and her father made no attempt to answer that down right lie.

'Why didn't you get engaged when he was here?' Sybil continued, pleasure uppermost in her voice.

'Neither of us thought of it then.'

22

'How wonderful that you feel absolutely sure now. Why, people are able to travel everywhere these days. No place on earth that is beyond reach if one has the money.' Sybil's vivacious manner implied that she was conjuring up a visit to Australia herself in the near future. She poured the coffee and set it down before them on the long, low table, swooping on the silver platter of chocolate cake and offering it to Melanie, her azure eyes bright. 'Have a slice?'

'I don't think I could manage it, thank you, Sybil, though it looks delicious.'

'Please, for me. I baked it especially.'

'Very well, then.'

'I'm so excited for you, dear,' Sybil went on, 'You can't imagine!'

Nigel Kent sipped at his coffee as though he was negotiating a difficult exercise. 'Melanie isn't married yet!' he said hardily. 'She may very well change her mind.'

'Nonsense!' Sybil said briskly, though her smile faded slightly. 'Melanie would be a fool to pass up such a catch—good-looking and rich, and he's mad about the girl. I'm going to do my best to persuade her!' Sybil sat down and dropped more sugar into her coffee than she intended. She was an attractive brunette in her mid-forties with a good figure and a lot of abilities, but her stepdaughter brought out the worst in her. There was a good deal of truth in Nigel's allegation that Sybil went in some awe of her stepdaughter, though her manner suggested just the opposite. It was disconcerting and thoroughly unsettling to have Melanie in the house. Made in her mother's image as she was, it kept Nigel

23

in some kind of bondage to the memory of his first wife. There was a great deal of difference between being a true wife and another woman's shadow. David Mac-Callister offered an honest escape for all of them.

Speculatively Sybil looked back at Melanie, finding such silvery beauty less unendurable than usual. Nicole had had just the same bone structure, delicate but clearly defined, the same pale floating hair, the same deeply green eyes with tiny flecks of gold in them, the surprisingly dark arching brows. Nicole herself, a misty wraith, seemed to stand behind her daughter, almost firming into a physical reality as Sybil watched. Sybil's hand trembled and she groped for the edge of the chair. The scent of roses seemed to fill the air—Nicole's favourites. Between them, Nicole and Melanie, Sybil's nerves were worn to a shred. She had loved Nigel since she had been a girl in her twenties, but Nigel had never known, which was just as well. The very thought would have startled him almost like some kind of sacrilege. He had always considered her attractive and good company; she was a member of his wife's charming circle of friends, but Sybil had had to work very hard indeed to gain his interest and change their relationship in the years following Nicole's tragic death. Sybil, considered by many people to be a good friend of the family, had actually resented Nicole intensely, loathing her shining fair enchantment, the way she always had of resting softly against her husband, his hand encircling her narrow waist, his dark eyes alive with his love for her.

After the shock of Nicole's death passed, Sybil had seen her miraculous opportunity. Not for nothing had she saved herself, though it had taken years before

Nigel even considered her in the light of companionship and another twelve months to offer a sober, carefully considered proposal. Her own physical attractiveness had done the rest. They would have a good marriage when Melanie was well out of sight. Her going away represented for Sybil a victory. So sensible was she of this that she would gladly have suggested to Nigel to pay the girl's fare, had not the MacCallisters been so exceptionally well off.

Melanie for her part was well aware of Sybil's inner exultance, and the reason for it. Poor Sybil! Now of all times she felt sorry for her. In order to win Sybil's acceptance she had to leave the country. It was almost funny. Moreover, Sybil had launched into pieces of advice, all designed to help Melanie get through her first weeks in a strange country.

'When are you leaving?' her father finally asked her, almost cringing from hearing.

'Thursday.'

'In less than a week?'

'It's all arranged,' Melanie said, her head bent.

'Goodness, I feel worn out!' he sighed.

'Really, Nigel, you should be thrilled and delighted that your daughter has such a splendid proposal tucked away in her belt,' chided Sybil.

'No man's too good for my daughter!'

Sybil laughed harshly, angry and jealous of the splendid fire in Nigel's dark eyes. 'Think of Melanie, dearest, not of yourself.'

Melanie scanned her father's face, knowing too well how he was feeling. She was feeling that way herself. Swiftly and gracefully she expressed her appreciation for all Sybil's efforts that evening, the beautifully presented meal that had tasted like sawdust, then she touched her high forehead, feeling the start of an emotional headache. 'I won't stay any longer. I have an hour's drive in front of me and a few things I must attend to, but of course I'll see you before I go.'

'My dearest child, I'll certainly be taking you to the airport.' Nigel Kent stood up abruptly. 'I'm sorry I haven't been more enthusiastic.'

'I know, Father, I know.'

Incredulously Sybil watched Nicole's daughter take up the same soft position against Nigel's side, Nigel's arm sliding round her, arousing all the old miserable recollections. How fortunate these soft women were who could tie a man so blindly to them. Any girl so strongly reminiscent of her mother was much better out of the way. Nigel would recover—she would see to it.

'Don't let's keep you, dear!' Sybil said, a slight edge to her voice.

'I'll come out to the car with you,' said Nigel, evidently disturbed.

Melanie turned her silver-gilt head over her shoulder. Not for the life of her could she have made the hypocritical gesture of kissing Sybil's cheek. 'Look after yourself, Sybil,' she managed. 'I know you look after Father well and I'm very glad of it.'

'Thank you, dear. I doubt if I'll get to the airport, but you know you have my blessings. Write to us. We'll be waiting for news.'

Melanie stared back at the glowing room for a moment, then she lifted her hand and followed her father out of the house. She was profoundly moved and in the darkness father and daughter embraced each other and fought down their tears. The past had ended for both of them and parting was painful. Melanie was going away from all that she had known, flying like a bird into the blazing Australian summer. Sheltered for most of her life, she would have to find herself in the shimmering heat among unfamiliar sights and sounds and a far different world.

That night she cried herself to sleep until she had no more tears left, but despite the heartbreak she had made her decision. She had agreed to go to Coorrabin, into David's waiting arms, but in her dreams a stranger, a man she had never seen, was there to meet her. She fought out of her dream, her skin burning, her heart thumping erratically against the nest of pillows. So real was her dream, so deeply disturbing, she almost thought she would recognise the man again. The rest of that strange night she passed fitfully and rose with the dawn light. Until the following Thursday it would be easiest to bury herself in her work.

CHAPTER THREE

WHEN Melanie emerged from the Custom and Immigration formalities, there was no David to meet her. Her green eyes, huge and fatigued, scanned the crowded lounge. Nearly everyone had somebody. All around her was the babble of voices, an atmosphere of drama, reunions and partings, the excitement of that fabulous long-awaited trip overseas. This was Darwin, gateway to Australia, so tragically devastated by a cyclone called Tracey, but risen again from the rubble, administrative capital of a half a million square miles of the Northern Territory, the Top End. Here the voices were different—lazy, relaxed, completely uninhibited. The place seemed to be swarming with tall, deeply tanned individuals in jeans and high boots and colourful shirts. These were the stockmen or cattlemen and they looked just like the cowboys of every Western type movie Melanie had ever seen.

A very pretty girl with mahogany hair and a gorgeous tan, a lei of what looked like wild orchids round her neck, suddenly pushed past Melanie and threw herself into the arms of the young man who had been seated across the aisle from Melanie. Looking into her half laughing, half crying, brightly glowing face, Melanie experienced a moment of complete abandonment. Where was David? In his last telephone call to her just before she left London he had promised to meet her as soon as she landed. Perhaps he was still fighting his way through the throng. Apart from feeling incredibly lost she would need him to help her manage her luggage. Anxiously she lifted the silken weight of her hair off her nape.

Darwin, she knew, was a frontier town and it was there in the multi-racial kaleidoscope of people; the 'British' faces, the Italian and Greek, the Chinese and Malays, a good sprinkling of aboriginal with their glossy skins and soft melodious voices, Polynesians and a trio of exotic young beauties behind the gift and souvenir counters with streams of inky black hair, copper skins and velvety eyes, a mixture of blood in their veins. Like a girl in a hurry as if she had some actual purpose she crossed to where the first loads of luggage were already being brought in. Her father had taken care of her luggage in London and she was hampered too by her outsize handbag. Any minute David would tap her on the shoulder and she would turn into his arms.

'Excuse me, are you Melanie?'

The voice was friendly, admiring, but in no way David's. She turned in surprise, looking up a considerable distance to a redheaded giant of a man, nearer fifty than forty, his skin tanned to a deep russet, his amiable blue eyes fanned by a hundred crinkles. Politely she smiled, though it was hard to maintain it, she was so disappointed.

'Yes, I am.'

'Fine. I knew it had to be you from Jay's description.'

'*Jay?*' She had put out her hand instinctively and the giant was pumping it, but very gently, so as not to hurt her, introducing himself at the same time.

'I'm Jock Drummond, Jay's foreman at Coulta.'

She felt slightly idiotic, but she had to repeat the unknown name. '*Jay?*'

'Why, Jay MacCallister!' her rescuer informed her, his blue eyes mirroring her perplexity. 'You know, Dave's brother. You *are* Melanie Kent, Dave's fiancée?'

'Well . . . yes. I didn't know David had a brother.'

'You didn't know he *had* one?'

Clearly she had stunned him, for his voice had risen and thundered powerfully, causing several heads to

29

turn. 'Excuse me, Miss Melanie, he *has* one!'

'David didn't tell me. Where is he?' She tried to look past Jock Drummond's huge frame, seeking in vain David's lean, elegant figure.

'I'm sorry to tell you, Melanie, your Dave has gone and broken his arm. His horse rolled on him—a kind of freak accident, just happened. I expect he was thinking of you and got careless. Jay's all tied up at Coorrabin until at least mid-morning tomorrow, so I've been given the very pleasant task of meeting you and welcoming you and taking you back to Coulta until Jay can fly in and collect you.'

The intensity of her shock and disappointment flashed out of her eyes. 'Jay is David's younger brother?' she asked.

'Jay is *MacCallister*!' Jock replied dryly, his humorous eyes registering her every reaction. 'He's the Boss. There isn't anyone in these parts that doesn't know that. *Dave* is the younger brother. There's another one too, Greg. Didn't Dave tell you?'

'I'm afraid not,' Melanie said faintly. 'He did tell me he had a sister.'

'So he has—Susan. She's married now and living on her husband's property in North Queensland. Know where that is?'

She smiled and it was like the sun on her face. 'I do. I've read up a good deal on all the States of Australia.'

'Good girl!' Jock found himself smiling as well. 'Now you just give me your baggage tickets and relax. I'll collect your luggage for you. Julie, that's my wife, is looking forward to meeting you. She's back at the homestead. I expect you'd like to rest up a little.'

'No, I feel fine,' Melanie assured him. 'A little tired maybe, but it was a good trip.'

In actual fact her mind was seething. It seemed incredible to her now that David had neglected to tell her about his all-important brother Jay. He hadn't even mentioned his younger brother Greg. There seemed no good reason why he should want to keep such information secret. Now he had broken his arm and Jay MacCallister was flying in to meet her. It was almost like her dream. She found herself trembling and she took a severe hold of herself.

Jock Drummond had turned his head back towards her, smiling reassuringly. He looked a very nice man, with a fatherly kind of tenderness in his expression as though he was used to attending to young lost creatures. She had been quite unprepared for his news, but his presence was a small comfort. She needed David desperately. Why had he told her so little of his real life? She was so tired, so emotionally spent from saying goodbye to her father that she doubted her future in this vast sunbaked land. She didn't want to be part of this vigour and outgoing life. She wanted to be back in her quiet room in London. Jock Drummond was still throwing reassuring backward glances to her, and she was touched by his consideration.

The jacket of her slack suit was much too hot in the heat, so she took it off, folding it through the handles of her bag. The satiny self-striped green of her blouse echoed the colour of her eyes. This touchdown in Darwin should have been a wonderful experience, but she felt as though the ground had been cut from beneath her feet. There was nothing to lift her heart, for all the colour and exotica around her the babble of different languages.

Fifteen minutes later they were speeding across country to Coulta Creek, the most northerly station in the MacCallister chain. Jock Drummond drove fast and well, keeping up the conversation but in fact filling Melanie in with a great deal of information he had somehow grasped David had neglected to. There were so many things he hadn't told her that after a while she began to feel bewildered. Jock spoke of Jay MacCallister with great respect and loyalty, almost as if he was the central figure in the world, but of David he was strangely reticent, for whatever reason.

The sun was dazzling like a great molten shield in the cobalt sky. Melanie had never experienced such a quality of light. The country seemed immense, great open tracts of grassy savannahs, then jagged purple and blue granite walls rising out of nowhere. They passed tropical parklands and natural springs, protected sanctuaries and silver glinting billabongs heavy with the most exquisite lotus lilies. The creeks and estuaries of the great tidal rivers concealed beneath just such lilies the powerful man-eating crocodiles. Buffaloes stood in the tall wheat grass and corellas in their glittering white hundreds decorated the branches of every tree, shrieking loudly as the big station wagon flew past them, throwing up dust. It was immensely exciting and despite herself Melanie began to respond like a tightly furled flower reacting to the sun.

'When I left London it was raining,' she said. 'This all seems like a dream—all this great emptiness and so very exotic. What's that mountain of blossom?'

'Bougainvillea. It grows everywhere in such profusion it has to be cut back or it would overrun everything.'

'It looks beautiful.'

'I suppose it is,' Jock said, taking another look at the towering pink mass of blossom. 'How does it sound to you, a life in the sun? You'll have to get used to the heat, I guess, and protect that lovely English complexion. I can say now I've seen an English rose.'

'Thank you, Mr Drummond,' she smiled.

'*Jock*, please. It's all very different from what you're used to?'

'It looks very romantic and challenging,' Melanie agreed.

'Lotus Land before the cyclone and we'll get back to it—at least for the pleasure-seekers, the tourists, the game-shooters, but we work darned hard on Coulta. Jay does a great job. He runs the chain even better than his dad, which is saying something indeed.'

Melanie hesitated, looking down at her hands. 'David helps him, of course.'

'Of course!' Jock glanced at her briefly. 'Jay does have a foreman on Coorrabin just as I am. His name is Len Murray, a good bloke. Len and I have been mates for years. He's one of the best cattlemen in the business. The Old Man had great faith in him, but running a big organisation takes a very special kind of man. Jay gives the orders and we follow them.'

'How old is he?' Melanie asked, feeling a little awkward.

'Oh, Jay must be thirty-four or five. He's been taking

so much responsibility for so long one forgets how old he is.'

'I gather he's quite a man.'

'Even the ladies think so,' Jock said, and smiled.

'He's not married?'

'I don't think he's had time to think about it up to date. There are plenty interested in him. He'd only have to snap his fingers!'

'Lucky man!' she said dryly.

'Don't let him scare you,' Jock said kindly.

'I won't—I *hope* I won't. I've only so recently learned of his existence.'

'I guess Dave was going to surprise you,' Jock said, trying to be kind but thinking his own thoughts. When it came down to bedrock Dave was just plain jealous of his brother, wanting to be number one, complaining all the time, but without Jay's stature. Not telling this little English girl about Jay was reacting in a peculiar way, yet it was natural to Dave. Jock gazed at her reflectively. She was trying to decide what she thought about it all. He could read her green eyes and he could see she had suffered a shock. With a daughter of his own about her age, he almost felt like leaning over and patting her hand. He had expected a pretty girl, but this slender nervous creature was really lovely, the sunlight shining on her very fair head, bent slightly and looking outwards at the flying miles. Scarcely anything about her seemed to link her with Dave. She seemed very gentle and sensitive and her voice fell like music on his ears. She was quite unlike any other woman Jock could think of, unless maybe Jay's mother, painted as a young woman. He looked at it every time he went up to the house, marvelling that there wasn't any physical trace of her in all three of her children, though Dave and Sue had blue eyes.

Jay was the Old Man all over again, but more approachable, less the recognised landed gentry, more contemporary in his outlook. Dave was the arrogant one, demanding respect everywhere when it was given automatically to his brother. Young Greg was developing nicely free of the self-inflicted frustrations that hounded Dave. Glory, his own daughter and a source of profound delight to him, was head over heels in love with Greg—not that it would do her much good. Glory would be considered quite boisterous beside this girl, her laughter bursting out of her at every other minute. Of course Melanie was tired after her long trip and she was suffering a very natural disappointment. There was a fragility about her that was apparent in fact she looked as if she had had about all she could take. Dave hadn't been honest or fair with her; he had undermined her feeling of security and faith in him.

Jock's mouth tightened as an indication as to the nature of his thoughts. Dave MacCallister created tension wherever he went. He was handsome enough with plenty of charm when he wanted it, but Jock had the vague idea he could cause this girl heartbreak. Perhaps he had been postponing mentioning his family until he met her at the airport, but now his intentions had been scattered by a freak accident. Jay would have to collect her.

Oh, lord! Jock thought a little hopelessly, and screwed up his eyes against the brilliant glint of the sun. Morning would arrive soon enough and Jay would be there to take charge. Always considerate, he told Melanie to put her head back and take a nap. They would be driving for over two hours. The less said about Dave and his shortcomings the better. It wasn't Jock's job to explain David MacCallister or question his motives. This girl had come all the way out from England to marry him and he hoped they would be very happy. A great pity, though, that she had to suffer this initial disappointment. He couldn't really blame himself. The sooner she knew about Jay the better. Jay always managed to put things right even for his bad-tempered brother. The whole situation was a bit tricky. What a damned selfish thing to do! It was just like Dave.

Melanie awoke to a fragrant brilliant morning and the sound of a million rapturous bird sounds; not songs as she knew them, but loud carolling calls, shrieks of ecstasy from the umbrella trees and cackling laughter from the gums. Hot sunshine streamed across the bed. She turned her head quickly, pushed back the tropical netting and found the clock. The Drummonds had let her sleep late. It was after nine o'clock. She slipped her long legs out of the bed and went to the window.

This new world was wonderful. The great tropical shade trees were swept with fiery blossom—poinciana, she had been told, and flame trees. The brilliant gold was cassia and cascara, the omnipresent bougainvillea breathtaking walls of pink and white and magenta. There was none of the pale tenseness of yesterday about Melanie. She looked very young and rested, her complexion flawless, a little languid with the warmth

36

of the sun raying through her right to the bone. An aboriginal house girl was in the yard beneath her shooing with her apron at Waddi, the Drummonds' pet emu. Melanie leaned further out the window to watch her and it was then she saw it, the sun glinting off the silver propellers. A twin-engined light aircraft, white with narrow red and blue stripes on the fuselage and tail, come to rest like some giant bird just beyond the perimeter of the homestead's grounds. Comprehension dawned immediately. It had to be MacCallister.

She couldn't dress quickly enough, filled now with a kind of excitement. She wished now she had not been allowed to sleep so late, but the Drummonds were the kindest, most hospitable people in the world. They had done everything in their power to put her at her ease and Glory, their daughter, had been irresistible in her warm friendliness, even vacating her room for the smaller guestroom, despite Melanie's protests. All of them had recognised her fatigue and disappointment and had insisted she have an early night. She had slept the clock round, when she had expected to toss and turn all night, her mind awhirl with so many discrepancies between what David had led her to believe and what the Drummonds had revealed in the course of conversation over the dinner table.

Such a different slant she had been given on Jason MacCallister, David's father! David had given her the strong impression that his father had been a very hard and exacting man with little time or love to spend on his son. The Drummonds, however, had obviously worshipped the ground he had walked upon, and were full of tales of him. Jason MacCallister, one, two and now three were Outback legends. The only fact that tallied was the MacCallister wealth and position, with Jay MacCallister, not David, running the family kingdom. Such inconsistencies were deeply disturbing and she had done her best to hide her bewilderment. What did it matter to her who ran the MacCallister organisation and occupied the seat of power? Why had David neglected to tell her about his brother? It made no sense at all, yet she must try to understand it. David had promised her happiness in this vast untamed world of his. She *had* to trust him, despite all the doubts that now assailed her. He had been so loving and considerate in London, such wonderful company, all his omissions seemed so much harder to accept.

Her thoughts strayed to what her father had said. What did she really know of David? Yet his letter had been ardent. He loved her and needed her—so important when she had felt so alone for a long time. Thinking this, she calmed, her anxieties submerged by her own warm tide of feeling. She could see David's blue eyes so dark and compelling, feel the urgent touch of his mouth. *You must come to me and stay with me— always!* His letters had decided her. Perhaps there was some kind of terrible conflict between the brothers? That would explain it—yet the Drummonds' allegiance to Jay MacCallister wouldn't have been more clear. It was the simplest, most natural thing in the world for them. Glory, with her smiling vivacity, had called David one of the most eligible bachelors in the country, but she had never tacked on 'what a lucky girl Melanie was' in the usual manner. Rather she had implied with her admiring faintly wry glances that

David was the lucky one. Melanie had thought her just trying to be kind.

It didn't seem possible that David's caresses had the traitor touch. She shouldn't allow one discovery to set such a chain of doubts in motion. She would reserve judgment on David until she had met his brother. David, very naturally, had wanted to impress her letting her believe he was in charge of Coorrabin, but it hadn't been necessary. The truth was always so much better. Probably at this moment he was writhing in shame and embarrassment. After all, had things gone according to plan, he would have met her at the airport and put matters straight, though even then it would have been too late. Perhaps David was more complex than she was ever aware—his behaviour certainly suggested it. It made her feel helpless. She only hoped he had an adequate explanation. It had taken a lot of faith in him to have come so far.

When Melanie left Glory's room, she looked fresh and immaculate, but her serenity on the outside only masked the hollow feeling of insecurity inside her. She walked along the corridor and into the hallway, her light steps noiseless on the carpet runner. It was then she heard a man's voice from the verandah and for the moment David was forgoten. She came to a dead stop, her heart racing. It was a very attractive voice, she realised that, dark and resonant, much crisper than any of the Drummonds', but somehow it made her afraid. The other voices chimed in—Jock's drawl, Glory's laughing contralto, her mother's, much lighter and higher in character.

39

'What's she like?' that crisp, cosmopolitan voice was asking.

'Beautiful!' Glory drawled appreciatively. 'I'll go and wake her in a minute. She was tired out. She's only a little thing—compared to me, anyway.'

'You can say that again!' Jock Drummond cut in. Glory, christened Lucy, was a strongly built girl with the Drummond springing red hair and bright blue eyes. She had a warm, exuberant manner that drew people naturally and made her nickname entirely in keeping with such a zestful young creature. Melanie had liked her at once.

'Dave's seething with discontent!' MacCallister offered, and seemed to laugh under his breath.

'I don't wonder!' This from Jock.

Melanie fell back a few paces, not wanting to go out on to the verandah at all. Didn't Australians realise how clear and carrying their voices were? Used as they were to the great outdoors, their voices, she was to learn, seldom fell to a discreet murmur.

'I bet he's really looking forward to today!' Glory said boldly. 'Melanie's the loveliest thing I've ever seen. Very English!'

'Really?' That sardonic dark voice again.

'And you pure Scot!' Jock Drummond was saying to his daughter.

'No matter!' MacCallister broke in. 'Undoubtedly we can give her the tender care she deserves.'

'I do hope they'll be very happy together!' Nell Drummond said with her nice, natural friendliness.

'You're going too far ahead, Nell. There's no talk of marriage as yet!'

In that instant Melanie hated Jay MacCallister with an unnatural violence. Her green eyes blazed and her head came up, proud and shining. She walked out on to the verandah to that dark, insolent man who was waiting for her, only vaguely conscious of the Drummonds and their warm greetings. She didn't realise she was staring. He stood up to face her with casual grace, meeting her eyes. His startling light glance began to sparkle as if he guessed the fury behind her set expression.

'Melanie! I thought you were going to sleep the day away!'

For a moment she lost all sense of time and place. Maybe her nightmare was going to go on for ever. She felt paralysed by her feeling of familiarity, the glittery gaze that was trying to fluster her still further. Then Glory said something that brought her back to full consciousness.

'Mr MacCallister.' She held out her hand and he moved towards her, looking down at her from his lean height. Melanie was amazed how alike and how unalike David he was. The family resemblance was strong, yet the expressions were so entirely different that such similarity in bone structure seemed negligible. This man's formidability was all too evident. Incredibly he was much better-looking than David, taller, harder, darker except for his strange light eyes. Here was a man more ruthless than David would ever know how to be. Her antagonism startled her, her sympathies and allegiance were all with David. Her smile had faded and she was glad he had released her hand. Her skin was burning. Those mocking, unchanging eyes were sizing her up, finding her wanting in some vital respect.

Her looks, such as they were, were obviously nothing to him, only the lamp to burn moths, and somewhat illogically she was resentful. Still her antagonism steadied her.

'It's very kind of you to come and get me,' she said, speaking formally. 'I'm sorry I slept so late, but I was rather tired after the long trip.'

'There was no other way, but I assure you it's a pleasure. Dave, of course, should have been at the airport to meet you, but you've heard his sad tale. He's as mad as a hawk to dip out at such an all-important time.'

'I miss him,' she said a little shortly, knowing that Glory was looking at her in surprise. Were her feelings so transparent? She turned around and smiled to make up for it. 'Mr and Mrs Drummond and Glory have been very kind to me. No one could have looked after me better, and I'd like to thank you again.'

'Yes, they're splendid people altogether!' MacCallister said with his impossible mockery that hurt her. 'When you've had breakfast, we'll get away. Take your time, there's no great rush.'

'Just be ready in ten minutes!' Glory warned dryly. 'You don't know this man. I'll attend to your packing, Melanie,' she offered with her engaging, faintly crooked smile.

'And I'll go and see to Melanie's breakfast,' Mrs Drummond chimed in, so tiny her husband had to bend over to drop a kiss on the crown of her head.

'Some coffee for Jay while you're at it, love.'

'Of course!' Nell Drummond bustled away and Jock began pushing chairs in.

'I've got that stock report ready for you, Jay. I'll go and get it.'

'Better or worse than I expected?' Jay enquired.

'Better,' Jock said with some satisfaction.

'Good man! We could do with a few breaks.'

Jock's deep rumble was laced through with triumph. 'Coulta will pull through,' he said.

'And I won't forget how much you've done!'

Jock rocked back on his high boots with pleasure, his all-over-russet face darkening with a quick rush of blood. 'That's nice of you, Jay.'

'What about you, Melanie, do *you* think I'm nice?' grinned Jay.

Jock laughed and went on his way, knowing Melanie was engaged in a little struggle with herself. Jay had an almighty impact sometimes.

'I haven't had time to form an opinion at all, Mr MacCallister.'

'Strange! I thought I got an instant reaction. I've apologised for not being Dave. What more can I say?'

Melanie found herself moving backwards as though it was safer that way. Never had she been more conscious of a man's regard, so cool and speculative. Surely he didn't think her an adventuress? A lot of people did get a little odd about their money, she knew that. She would hate to be here on this man's approval, or subject to his icy scorn. There seemed no getting away from the fact that he was head of the family. He could make people toe the line with one clap of his hands, but she wasn't surrendering to his prejudiced attitudes. God, she was nervous!

He held out a chair for her with elaborate courtesy

43

and she sank into it, preferring to stand but knowing it would have made her seem foolish. 'Dave was right!' he said pleasantly. 'A blind man could see you're beautiful!'

'But unsuitable!' She couldn't resist that.

'Did I say that, Melanie?—and you must call me Jay, as you're one of the family.'

'Which arm did David break?' she asked abruptly. 'Mr Drummond wasn't sure.'

'The right. Perfectly easy to do if you've got your mind on something else.'

'You've never had an accident?' She let her eyes rest on him lightly. He was so tall she was getting a crick in her neck. Why didn't he sit down as well?

'A few,' he said, obliging her as though he could read her thoughts. 'Do I detect a grain of censure?'

'I'm sorry, but you seem so ... uncaring!'

'I care all right. I'm a man short!'

'I see,' she said dryly.

'No, you don't see, little English girl, but who knows, one day you might. Tell me, do you love my brother?'

'Am I required to answer?'

'Don't you think it's my business?'

His silver eyes dared her to deny it. Instead she shook her pale head. 'Do you always talk like this, Mr MacCallister?' she asked.

'How's that, Miss Kent?'

'With such authority—high-handedly.'

'I guess it's my training!' He drawled for the first time and she could see his hard charm. 'Try not to let it bother you—and you didn't answer my question.'

'I've come a long way,' she said as though that was an answer.

'Go on.'

'I'm almost certain I love him,' she went on.

He flashed a glance over her face. 'You're sure a few other factors didn't influence your decision?'

'Such as?'

'I understand your father's remarriage came as a shock to you.'

'On the contrary, Mr MacCallister, I was prepared for it.'

'But you didn't like it, just the same—or more pertinently, your stepmother didn't like you. It must have been an uncomfortable situation.'

There was a cool hard look in his shimmering eyes and colour touched her cheeks. 'What has that to do with my feeling for David?'

'*David?* Lucky David. I'm only trying to get at the truth, for your sake as much as his. I don't want to see you flounder any more than Dave.'

'I don't really care what you think,' Melanie said coldly.

'Yes, you do—I can see it in your eyes. Don't worry, I'm not the ogre Dave no doubt made me out to be. Not all the time, anyway.'

Out of loyalty to David she didn't tell him he hadn't been mentioned at all. She had a feeling he would think that contemptible. There seemed no way she could defend herself when he had obviously disapproved of her on sight. 'Am I really so unsuitable?' she found herself asking.

Jay MacCallister didn't smile. 'You're lovely. I can see how you've turned Dave's head.'

She tried hard not to show how hurt she was. 'Am I to learn early that you say whatever pleases you?'

He considered this, his arrogant dark head on one side. 'Don't let me hurt you. In return you can let me know what you think any time you like.'

'Perhaps you consider the English too conservative?'

'You're welcome to think us very outspoken.'

'I hope I'm more charitable!' Her heart was pounding and she knew he was mocking her.

'Don't worry, Miss Kent,' he said. 'I've nothing against the English. I've got too many relations there.'

'You're just in an odd mood?'

'No, I'm always like this. I've not the slightest objection to your trip out here.'

'No, of course not—especially, as you pointed out yourself, as there's no talk of marriage yet.'

His brilliant gaze searched for hers and his mouth twisted in a humorous grin. 'So you were eavesdropping?'

'Certainly not!' Melanie was staring at him unconsciously, noting the bronze skin, the thick eyelashes, the arrogant set of his head, the straight nose like David's, the harder, firmer mouth and chin. 'Australians don't realise how very clearly they speak.'

'No kidding! Your own voice is like a silver bell.'

'I didn't expect you,' she explained.

'What a surprise you were in for!' Jay drawled.

No surprise, she could have told him. I dreamt about you. So splendid and terse. Where was David, her salvation? For a moment she looked almost forlorn, her slender young body taut in the chair.

His silver eyes narrowed, flicking over her lovely, downbent face. 'My objection is this, Melanie, and please look at me. David—God! you've got me saying it—*Dave*' he started again, 'has responsibilities, a position to fill and maintain. Our life is here in the Outback. It's not easy. One has to be born to it. You couldn't, if you stayed and married Dave, be running off to the cities all the time, and that's what you are, a city-bred girl. You could find our way of life too lonely, too isolated, maybe, at times, too violent. To think of marriage at this stage is plain crazy.'

'But David loves me,' she protested.

'So he says. He's been in love before.'

'He told me I was his life, his hope for the future.'

'No wonder he's in such agony now! You don't look it, but you must be a very determined young woman.'

'How do I look?' she challenged him rather bitterly. 'A silly celluloid doll?'

'Not with those finely bred bones. Relax, child— were you so unhappy at home?'

'I found it very hard to leave my father.'

'I can see that, yet you've come all this way to be with Dave?'

'He paid my way, as you must know.'

'Yes.'

'I couldn't afford it myself and my stepmother would have been furious if my father gave me the money as he wanted to.'

'The money's no problem. Personalities and their interaction are another thing again.'

'Are you trying to panic me?' she said dryly.

'No, I'm warning you in advance. You and Dave mightn't suit. It could happen.'

'Then why make it sound so dangerous?'

'Some women can bring chaos without even meaning

47

to. You might be one of them with your leafy green eyes.'

Melanie tried to speak reasonably. It was necessary to accept that his influence would be strong. David was obviously scared of him. She was scared of him herself. His eyes were searing the skin off her. 'I know this is a sort of gamble,' she said quietly, 'that either of us could risk disillusionment, but you're trying to shake what little confidence I have left.'

He cast her such a quick look she had to move back. 'Now I don't understand *you*. You must have had plenty of confidence to come all this way.'

'I believe I love David!'

'I hope you do!' His mouth tightened—a beautiful mouth, firm and chiselled, but hard.

'You mean that?' she cried in a sudden anguish of disbelief.

'Why wouldn't I? Dave needs a settling influence— not that you appear to fit the bill in that respect. It would have been all too easy for him to lose *his* head. What about you?'

'Surely you know your own brother?'

'Yes, I do. What qualities in Dave do you admire, apart from the obvious ones?'

'I don't have to answer that!' It was certain he meant Dave's looks and money. MacCallister money.

'Try to,' he coaxed. 'I'm listening.'

'David needs me!' she said as though that explained everything.

Jay suddenly hit the table, making her jump. 'God, what a fool I was not to realise it at once!'

48

'It's *you* I could never care for!' she burst out, shocked.

'That's the price of escape!' he said obscurely.

Her hand was shaking and she seemed to be losing her self-control. Others might admire and respect Jay MacCallister, but she found him frightening, with his silver glances like a blaze of lightning and just as destructive.

He stared out at the garden rather broodingly, then back at her. 'Do you find the heat distressing?' he asked.

'I haven't had all that much time to notice it.'

'Your cheeks are very hot,' he observed. 'I hope you've brought a sensible wide-brimmed hat. Sunstroke is no joke. For better or worse you're here to discover whether you can take it.'

'And you're going to try to make it harder?'

'Listen to you, Melanie!' he scoffed at her. 'You may need me before the year's over. Don't let your antagonism run away with you.'

'What way might I need you?' She met his challenging, faintly pitying gaze.

'Tell me the moment you want out!'

'Why should I want out at all?'

'You mightn't at all. You *have* comitted yourself to a degree Dave has never learned how to take no for an answer.'

'You're almost suggesting he lacks self-control. We got on wonderfully well in London.'

'A far cry from Coorrabin.' His mouth was faintly contemptuous. It seemed to tell her a lot. No wonder David found it so necessary to assert himself with such

49

a brother! He was making her feel as limp as a dish-rag. Perhaps he controlled all the finances, and here she was, the jumped-up little adventuress, trying to marry an heir to the MacCallister fortunes. She had fallen in love with David, not the MacCallister image. Sometimes such images grew to be an obsession. Why couldn't Jay greet her pleasantly, welcome her into the family, and leave well alone? This seemed the final humiliation, his disapproval.

'Go on. Go on,' he invited her. 'Say what you're thinking.'

'Perhaps I'm involving myself in more than I thought,' she confessed.

'You surely couldn't have been naïve enough to think it was all going to be a bed of roses, a modern fairytale. Knight sends in a plane to sweep off his love and they all live happily ever after?'

'Sounds wonderful, but I suppose it never happens.'

'You *look* very romantic, Melanie,' he told her. 'In some ways you're a gift, but unhappily we're far removed from your natural habitat. There's nothing under glass at Coorrabin!'

'What sort of answer is that?' she demanded.

'A realistic one!'

'I suppose I should be much interested in your ideas and opinions?'

'Unquestionably!' He smiled at her and it was just as she thought— David's charm on another scale, more controlled and masterful. She was suddenly afraid she might be showing that recognition. The most wonderful trip of her life had plunged her into a dilemma. She found herself in a world of family conflicts, of wealth

50

and power, of cynicism and having one's every motive questioned. She didn't look brazen or shameless, but Jay MacCallister looked as proud as the devil. Perhaps he had the right candidate already picked out for David, a member of his own exclusive circle. Somewhere at the back of her head Melanie had a faint memory of David's mentioning a girl's name. She should have listened, but he had been very offhand. It had been nothing serious at all, some girl and boy thing that had faded away.

'You're not married yourself?' she asked feelingly.

'Why, would you consider me?'

She flushed angrily, her green eyes glowing and enormous in her small face. 'No, indeed!'

'Then we're minus that problem. Actually, Melanie, I haven't had time to let my mind wander.'

'It must be dull, work all the way,' she commented.

'I know you're not trying to be provocative.'

'No, I'm not. I've come all this way to be with *David*, and of course, meet his family.'

'Of course,' he said suavely. 'Just how much of his close family life did Dave reveal to you?'

'Not as much as I might have wished,' she said guardedly.

'It was my instinctive reaction that you didn't know about me at all!'

Melanie seemed to lose colour, but she was quick to respond. 'Now why would you say that?'

He shrugged his wide shoulders. '*You* might have to guess a few things about Dave. I know it all. However, you're right in this—he does believe he loves you.

51

A few months on Coorrabin should resolve the situation.'

'As long as it suits your plans,' she said dryly.

'I don't know,' he said buntly. 'I'm just trying to be fair. I know women like to indulge in romantic fantasies ... see new places!'

Antagonism and a sense of futility flowed over her. 'Please talk about something else,' she begged.

'Have you brought your trousseau with you?' His dark voice was challenging and she stared back at him, stunned.

'You take it so absolutely for granted that I must answer you. You're not David's father, you're his brother!'

'I try in every way I know,' Jay agreed.

'And I didn't realise you ran the whole show!'

His brief laugh was cynical. 'Would it have altered your decision?'

'Had I met you in London with David, very likely, *yes*!'

'Thank you.' He shifted his position and she almost flinched away from him, a fact Jay wasn't slow to miss. 'However, I did invite you to be frank!'

'I couldn't match your ruthless candour, Mr Mac-Callister.'

His eyes skimmed her silvery blonde perfection with no sign of appreciation. 'If you're going to keep on calling me Mr MacCallister, I'll have to call you Miss Kent.'

'We usually take longer in England over first names,' she explained.

'Everyone knows that. But not here. *Days* might be considered a bit stuffy!'

Melanie could see from the glitter in his eyes that he was determined to needle her and she tried not to become foolishly heated. 'I sincerely hope you had no one else in mind for David. The thought has only recently crossed my mind.'

He laughed, a mocking, dancing light in his eyes. 'I'd give anything to see him settled. Frankly you're not the type I would have picked out for him. There was one girl, yes.'

'Should I have heard her name?' she asked.

'You'll hear it, I imagine. Her family are our closest neighbours.'

'Tell me now.'

'Hilary,' he said, and looked at her, a hard look that pined her. 'Hilary Lyall–Watson.'

'And you approve of her?' The question was brittle and instantaneous.

'I'm not such a fool that I meddle in arranged marriages, but there's a lot more to it than moonshine, silky hair and emerald eyes. Hilary is a countrywoman. She can ride and shoot and cut cattle as well as her brothers. She's had an excellent education and when she's dolled up she can even look glamorous.'

'A paragon!' commented Melanie.

'She hasn't got what you've got, but some rounds would definitely be hers.'

'An old pioneer family?' she asked, her voice cool and excessively English.

'Oh no, quite recent, but rich. They paid a monstrous price for the property.'

53

'David doesn't love her,' she said with certainty.

This apparently made him angry, for his black winged brows came together. 'He was pretty fond of her once.'

'*Fond?*'

'As in keeping her out until three o'clock in the morning. They were good friends as well. Hilary has qualities Dave lacks.'

'Such as?'

'I'll leave you to find that out, camellia face. That's what you're here for—to decide whether you and Dave are right for one another. Who knows, I might dance at your wedding.'

'We haven't got off to a good start,' she shrugged.

'I'm not entirely displeased,' he said. 'You don't have to be afraid of me, Melanie.'

'How can I not be when you seem to enjoy being king of the castle!'

'That doesn't make me out a monster!' he said with cool deliberation.

She searched his dark face unwillingly. Premonitions were strange. She had known in advance this man would turn out to be far more than she could possibly handle. 'Far from flying into a dream,' she said wryly, 'I seem to have hit harsh reality!'

'Wait until you see Dave. Family can be terrifying, but a lover is different. Remember you deserve what you get!'

'So you seem intent on telling me. I deserve a little courtesy and consideration as your guest.'

'And you'll get it. You're not my guest yet. Just Jock and Nell's!'

'Then I can tell you I share your lack of enthusiasm.'

'First impressions are often deceptive!' he said sardonically.

'One can only hope so. If your manners get no better, I'll have to go back to London, and I might take David!'

The silver-grey eyes studied her with more insolence than admiration. 'Do you think you could do it?'

'Give me a little credit, Mr MacCallister!' she begged.

His mouth twisted mockingly. 'Oh, I give you a lot, Dave's money is tied up and most of it's working.'

'I'm not interested in David's money!' she said, her green eyes flashing.

He gave her the straight look she would always remember. 'We all like to credit ourselves with the purest motives, but really——! I bet Dave treated you to all the best places, showered presents on you? Money just slides through his fingers.'

'It doesn't slide through mine!'

'All the better, the prospect of having some. We all need it.'

For a long moment Melanie looked at him, the colour coming under her skin. 'I thought Australia was supposed to be a classless society?'

'As classless as you'll find anywhere in the world, but money speaks the same language everywhere. There are drawbacks for the rewards. A poor man knows he's being married for himself.'

'I'm glad David has more faith in me than you have!'

Jay's eyes had a curious, considering look. 'Suppose we were to start again, Melanie. You don't have to look at me as though there's been some ghastly miscarriage of justice. I don't want to upset you.'

'You *have*!' He was only feet from her, very definite and masculine, with an air of world experience.

'Then you're much too sensitive,' he said lightly. 'You have that look about you.'

'I've had no experience of ...'

'... don't say it!'

'I can't imagine what you thought I was going to say.'

He laughed, his silver eyes flaring. 'It didn't look too flattering. I can't help it if I don't see that you and Dave were made for each other, but there's no reason why we can't be friends.'

'I don't believe in opposites attracting, Mr Mac-Callister.'

'I didn't say *attracting*, exactly!' A mocking expression replaced the smile in his eyes. 'Surely that doesn't seem proper in the circumstances?'

Melanie moved fretfully, losing her limpid coolness. 'I suppose I'm taking you much too seriously and you're just a notorious tease. Vigorous and *unsubtle*!'

'Why, Melanie!' he protested, easing back in his chair. 'Now you've hurt *me*! Just remember, if you need help don't think you can't come to me. Here's Nell with your breakfast. I propose leaving you so you can eat it in peace.' He stood up, looking down at her, and Melanie was struck again by the casual, fluid grace of his movements.

'Nell!' he called over his shoulder. 'Be a good girl and bring the coffee down to the office.'

'Of course, Jay. I'll be with you the minute I've fixed up Melanie.'

Inexhaustibly kind, Nell Drummond, her blue-grey

56

eyes gentle, began setting out Melanie's breakfast, English style as they preferred themselves, murmuring encouraging things all the while, then she took herself off. Inside Melanie was trembling, but she sat quietly, trying to do justice to her breakfast. Her mind wasn't functioning too clearly. Why in sweet heaven should she feel so threatened by this man called MacCallister? It wasn't as though he was cold and unfriendly. He wasn't, but his unassailable self-assurance was so powerful it was almost tangible. He was confident as no man she had ever met was confident. He confused her, but he had given her no real reason for feeling the way she did. Why couldn't he have been someone quite different? An earnest and friendly, more mature version of David instead of a man to stir up cross-currents?

Melanie buttered a wedge of toast and looked up to see Glory coming through from the hallway with two pieces of Melanie's very new-looking luggage in each hand. 'You didn't have to do that!' Melanie protested.

Glory gave her warm friendly smile. 'No trouble. I'm a big strong girl, as you can see!'

For some reason it came out with a hint of self-disparagement, and Melanie looked back at her with surprise. 'You're tall, certainly, but your figure is splendid!'

'Well!' Glory exclaimed. 'You're good for my morale. My only concession to the beauty game is keeping a hat on when I'm out in the sun. Apart from the freckles the sun would fade my hair out to a burnt orange like Dad's.'

'It's beautiful hair,' said Melanie. 'A real glory!'

'Couldn't manage all your breakfast?' Glory put the bags down and flopped rather than sank gracefully into an old planter's chair, the yellow canvas clashing wildly with her fiery hair.

Melanie glanced at her and smiled. 'I'm a bit nervous, I suppose.'

'Of Jay?'

'Well, yes. He doesn't remind me a good deal of David.'

'Oh, the three brothers are all different,' said Glory. 'Goodness me, yes! Jay's always had the big role to play. As he's the eldest and his father's successor life's been tough for him in lots of unexpected ways. Of course he's the Boss and he gets all the credits that go with it, but then too he has to shoulder all the responsibilities. It was hell after the cyclone. Darwin suffered dreadfully and the effects of it are still being felt. Jay was marvellous. People speak very highly of him. He's always right there with a helping hand. He took off loads of kids until their parents could come for them.'

'Yes, he certainly looks rugged and his shoulders are wide,' Melanie agreed.

'Dave now,' Glory continued conversationally, 'plays it smart and gets away for lots of breaks, but Jay is committed to running the chain—no holidays for him. You'll like Greg when you meet him. He's different again. I'm a bit soft about Greg, and I have been these many years since I lost my pigtails!'

'And how does Greg feel about you?'

'Only very moderately fond,' Glory replied soberly. 'Anyway, he's a MacCallister and I'm only the foreman's daughter. The MacCallister men are booked up well in advance, social machinations and so forth. Such a highly eligible young gent as Greg is unlikely to look my way and I'd better get used to it.'

'Life's full of surprises!' Melanie observed.

'Now isn't it! Anyway, good for you, Melanie. I'm hoping and hoping you'll stay—that you and Dave get married, I mean.'

'Well, we'll find out soon enough. Tell me about David's sister.'

'Sue?' Glory's reddish-brown eyebrows shot up. 'Daddy's little daughter. Old Jason was very fond of her. He spoilt her dreadfully. He was an indulgent father altogether except where Jay was concerned. Jay he was hard on—surprising when you consider he loved Jay best of all.'

Melanie tried to eat another piece of toast for appearances' sake, but couldn't. 'So they were all one big happy family!' she said rather tonelessly. 'I had an altogether different picture of David's father!'

'Tell me,' said Glory.

'Oh, I thought he might have been the sort of man to take a hard line with his sons, very difficult to please and exacting.'

'Well, he was in a way, but not nearly so much with the younger boys and not at all with Susan. Jay, it so happens, goes fairly easy on Dave—too easy, I'd say, and I know them. Living on Coorrabin will give you a more accurate picture, Melanie. I'll fill you in with a few details. It's better than nothing. Take each day as it comes. You'll love Coorrabin. The homestead is beautiful, out of this world. It will surprise you when you see it, set down in the wilds. Those old pioneer families did themselves proud as soon as they were able. The squatter's home was his castle. I'm envious of you. I'd give anything to be staying up at the house, but I'm not used to that kind of life. Sue always looked down her nose at me. A regular little snob is our Sue, not like the boys at all. I suppose it was that snooty school she went to and all the snobby friends she brought home from time to time. Anyway, the last time Dad saw her he said she had improved with marriage. There was plenty of room for it, if you ask me! I suppose I shouldn't say that, but I feel we're friends already and I know you'll treat it as confidential. Besides, you need to be clued up a bit better than you are. A girl needs to be prepared!'

Melanie saw the truth of this and sighed. 'Perhaps I've been brought out to be given the once-over!'

'I'd say so!' Glory answered promptly. 'But you've nothing to fear. You'll knock their eyes out and you're a real lady.'

'What's a real lady?' Melanie asked with a smile. 'I would call your mother a real lady.'

'Gee, thanks. Mom's great—but you know what I mean. The swanky accent and all your nice little ways. You could take your place easily at Coorrabin, mix with all Sue's friends and better still take the shine out of them.'

'But they won't be there, surely?'

'They'll turn up!' Glory promised darkly. 'If you and Dave are going to settle for each other, you'll be joining the organisation, in a manner of speaking. You'll have to front up and they'll swarm down on top of you to register their vote. You won't have any trouble with the men. Sue's husband, Derryn, is a real nice bloke, though he's one of them. Men always are nicer than women—you know, they accept you and they're friendly. Women are always affected by silly things, clothes and houses and possessions, like there was no other way. A lot of them value things I wouldn't value at all. I was invited to Sue's wedding—Jay put in a good word for me, I expect, because it couldn't have been Sue—and you should have seen some of her friends appraising me and my clothes. It was the best dress Mom ever made and I thought I looked brilliant. There were a few gracious old girls there, of course, but Sue's friends—ugh!'

'Perhaps you were too glowing!' Melanie suggested, feeling Glory's youthful pangs. 'No one could overlook you.'

'You're not kidding?'

'Can't you see that I'm not! Generally speaking the plainer a women is the easier it is for her to have ranks of women friends. It's human nature, I suppose, to fear a competitor. A lot of women are territorially minded. I've suffered on that account myself.'

'Well, you make me feel attractive,' said Glory, 'but *they* didn't. They made me feel a great gawky cowgirl, all those perfectly wonderful people with their money and the big properties they controlled. Why, the Mac-Callisters have as much or more than any of them, but Jay now is as easy and gallant as a Southern gentleman. He's the best boss in the world. You'll learn early how to judge his true worth. Jay's pure gold, and Greg's shaping up nicely as well.'

'What about David?' Melanie asked gently, then

wished she hadn't, for Glory flushed violently.

'Oh, I'm sorry, Melanie. I didn't mean anything by that—I've got no tact at all. It's too bad. Dave's fine, of course he is, but he's not as easy to get on with as Jay and Greg. I like him, honestly. I can understand how you fell in love with him.'

'Let's hope we both feel the same when we meet again. This isn't London!'

'No.' Glory glanced at Melanie shrewdly, then away again. 'You know, I've never had the yen to travel, even if we could afford it, which we can't. I'm so at one with all this. I love it, my home. I've never had a single desire to live anywhere else. Do you think that's odd?'

'No, of course not. Some people put down their roots deeply. I love travelling myself, but it was a great wrench to leave home.'

'I don't think I could ever leave Mom and Dad,' confessed Glory. 'Not for any great length of time or distance. I'm a real crybaby. All the time I was at boarding school I felt right out of my element. I longed and longed for the holidays. I can't wait to get out of the cities.'

'You never feel lonely?' asked Melanie.

'I'm too busy. Of course one day I want a home and family of my own not so far away that my kids won't have doting grandparents. I say, I'm an idiot, aren't I? You have tears in your eyes.'

'Then I'll brush them away. I hope you get everything you long for, Glory. I'm looking forward to talk-to you on the ... what was it?'

'Galah sessions. You know what a galah is, don't you?'

62

'A parrot.'

'A soft grey with an overall pink head. When you hear them start squawking in a group you'll realise where the term came from. Sometimes it's the only contact we women have for months on end. All the social occasions we live up like nobody's business. The MacCallister picnic race-day ball is the event of the year. Staff families and friends travel for hundreds of miles.'

'How far apart are the stations?' asked Melanie.

'You'll be flying most of the day. The Track, the highway from Darwin to the Alice, is a thousand miles long. Coorrabin is about six hundred nautical miles from here and the Baron does about two hundred or two-thirty knots. You'll be going in style. It's the Rolls of the light aircraft. We have a Cessna 180. It belongs to the station, of course. I don't know if Jay's going to stop at Coraki. If he does you'll be going out of your way. It's about three hundred miles from here in a south-easterly direction. You're off to the Channel Country, didn't you know? About a thousand miles inland from the State capital, Brisbane. Adelaide, the capital of South Australia, is actually nearer.'

'David just told me south-western Queensland. It's hard to grasp its size.'

'From Brisbane to Cairns in the far north is the same distance from London to Leningrad, then there's the rest of Cape York left. Two thousand miles from the tip to the border, nearly three-quarters of a million miles in all. You're in the Territory now and you'll be crossing our border. The Channel Country is unique. It's the home of the mighty cattle barons, the giant cattle kingdoms of four and more thousand square miles. You won't know what distance is until you're out on the great flood plains. You won't know what beef is until you've tasted Georgina beef. The three main rivers, the Diamantina, Georgina and Cooper flow for hundreds of miles, dividing and subdividing into a maze of gullies and channels. In drought times you can drive across twenty miles of the dry river beds, but when the rains come—brother! The whole country's under-water. It's a vast natural irrigation system and when the waters abate you and the birds are in heaven. Wild-flowers to the horizons! You can't imagine it.'

Glory went on, 'El Kedra, about two hours' flying time from here, is on the edge of the Simpson. It's a frightening and fascinating place, the Dead Heart. A land of mirage and fiery sand dunes and appalling heat!'

Glory broke off abruptly as Jay MacCallister and her father came back along the verandah, still deep in dis-cussion. Glory looked at them both a bit anxiously, hoping the report had justified all her father's hard work. Extremely competent as a cattleman, he was irritated by office work and all that went with it. She had typed the report herself.

Jock Drummond looked up and smiled at her happily and Glory began to rock herself gently. 'Hallelujah!'

For some reason Melanie found herself flushing, as she encountered MacCallister's lightning glance. 'All set?'

'Yes.' She stood up and began stacking the breakfast dishes back on the tray.

'I'll do that!' Glory began to help her, then waited to take the tray.

'Tell your mother!' Jock said briskly. 'We'll all walk down to the plane.'

CHAPTER FOUR

THEY had been flying for two hours and the lush savannahs had given way to a savage wilderness. Melanie was beginning to feel there was no one left in the world but the two of them. Grim stories of the desert began to ring in her ears. It was far more exciting to fly through this primeval land, the great brown ochre plains that stretched away to eternity. It was almost impossible to grasp immediately the dimensions of the country, its frightening loneliness and harsh magnificence, but to her credit she looked calm, strapped into the co-pilot's seat of the six-seater light aircraft. It was a far call from the comfortable reclining seat of an international jumbo jet, but to Jay Mac-Callister it was a routine part of life.

Once or twice as the plane moved up and down, riding the thermal currents, she felt vaguely nauseated, but MacCallister quite evidently was used to it. 'All right?' He glanced sidelong at her pale face.

'A bit uneasy now and then when we hit those air pockets!'

'You'd have had a far bumpier ride in the Cessna,' he assured her.

'Have you another plane?' she asked.

'Of course. Two others, as a matter of fact. They're essential—a Cessna, a Cardinal and a Beechcraft Bonanza. You're getting the royal treatment. I don't want you to arrive all jolted and shaken. I use the Baron for business trips, inter-state flying. It's bigger, it's pressurized, which means we can climb to ten thousand feet, and it's twice as fast as the others.'

'Incredible!' Melanie murmured. 'You make it sound like catching the bus!'

'It's a way of life out here. We have to have some way to cover the vast distances. Light aircraft have revolutionised the Inland. We use them for everything—moving men and gear, mustering, finding strays, boundary riding. In the old days that used to take a team of men weeks, now it can be done in a few short hours.'

'Have you all got a licence?' she asked.

'A full ticket, which means one's rated for instruments. In rugged country in a small plane there's no margin for error. One has to know one's environment, weather conditions, cloud formations and what they can do to a plane. A pilot is as much at the mercy of the air around him as a sailor is of the sea. Neither suffer fools gladly—there are far too many accidents to prove it. One must be fully prepared to go to sea or take to the skies. The training schools set high standards,' he added. 'Sue, my sister, chickened out after the simulator course, far too early, but in a way I'm glad she did. She hasn't the temperament to cope with an emergency and just making one silly error could be fatal. Derryn, her husband, does all the routine flying, and even Der-

66

ryn leaves all the difficult stuff, the round-ups and such like, to a professional pilot on his staff, a chap called Alan Neilsen.'

Melanie flashed up a quick look. 'Shall I be meeting your sister and her husband?'

'I can't think why not.'

'An inspection team?'

His eyes were like diamond chips. 'Did I say that? When it happens it will all be in a relaxed, family fashion.'

'I apologise.'

'So you should! Your eyes are as clear as a spring-fed pool, and just as green!'

Her throat went curiously dry and she hastened to change the subject. 'I wanted to ask you if you intend stopping at Coraki.'

'You're pronouncing it wrongly. The accent is on the first syllable. *No,*' Jay tacked on crisply, shaking his black head. 'It will be a long enough day for you, full of movement and secret yearnings. Dave is so excited you would hardly believe it.'

'I suppose he was impatient that he couldn't come?'

'You bet,' he said laconically, and smiled, his teeth very white against his tan.

'Was it a bad break?' she asked.

'He was in a lot of pain when I left. Swearing his head off—not deliberately, you understand, but at his ghastly piece of luck. The doc was flying in to look after him. I certainly hope he'll be in better spirits when we get back. Who knows, perhaps journey's end might mark your engagement. I know he'd marry you on the spot.'

'I'm not rushing into anything, Mr MacCallister,' she said, with an inexplicable rush of panic.

'Wise girl!' He exaggerated his drawl.

'*You* haven't!' she accused him.

'Rushed into anything? No, indeed. I haven't refrained from enjoying a woman's company, however. Why frown, Miss Melanie? There's nothing wrong in that, is there?'

'I wasn't frowning.'

'You *were*! It's nothing to do with sincerity. I always say at the start that I don't mean or feel marriage!'

'I think you'd make an insufferable husband!' Now why had she said that? His aura of challenge was so strong she had been provoked into forgetting her tongue.

'Damn! I'm offended. Could you please explain yourself, Melanie? It's really rather important.'

'Perhaps *too* dominant men can only hurt a woman,' she said hesitantly.

'Oh no, you've got the wrong number! I've a heart of gold.'

'I can't seem to think so.'

'And when did you hear of me, Melanie, the day before yesterday?'

'Whenever I did, Mr MacCallister, it was my *big* moment!'

'Call me Jay, just as an experiment,' he invited.

'Jay.'

'I suppose that's right! It doesn't sound the same.'

'Jay,' she said again, trying to alter the sound to Glory's rich drawl.

He laughed, a mocking, disturbing sound that had her saying passionately:

'I can't help my accent!'

'And I'm not looking to criticise it, little English girl. You have a delightful speaking voice, as I'm sure you know.'

'That's a comfort!' She hoped her cheeks weren't as flushed as they felt. She was afraid of this man Mac-Callister because she couldn't see the way ahead with him. He was so bracing, with his dark handsome face. She had tried a dozen times to superimpose her remembered imagine of David over him and failed. Jay MacCallister was startlingly vivid and for this reason he was dangerous. She felt as if she was constantly warding his personality off or it would envelop her like the clouds over which they were riding.

He was speaking now, *down* to her, as if he was about to give her a lecture. 'When we get to Coorrabin you can place a call to your father. It will make him feel better.'

'That's very kind of you!' she said in surprise.

'Not at all. I can imagine how he feels about you. I'd feel uneasy myself letting you junket around the world!'

'I've been looking after myself for a good while now,' she said.

'Really? You look fresh out of school. When was this anyway—since your father remarried?'

'No. I *was* at school then. I lived at home for another year after that, then I found I couldn't take it any longer.'

'Jealous of your new stepmama?'

'No, I had no such passion. I hope you believe me. Before she married my father, Sybil never said a word in the wrong place or made a false move. That came after—an unending series of them. My father and I had been living very quietly after my mother died. Sybil had been one of my mother's circle of friends, as far as *that* goes, it wasn't until after she married Father that she took an instant dislike to me. I'm very much like my mother to look at, as it happens!'

'Well, I can see that might well invite problems,' he agreed. 'You obviously need somebody to take good care of you, and you're hoping it will be Dave?'

'Why not?'

His attitude made Melanie answer more flippantly than she ever meant. She was naturally a serious and introspective girl, but she was making herself sound something of an opportunist.

'Your beauty at least is unparalleled in Dave's experience,' Jay MacCallister said rather sardonically.

'David and I were good friends in London,' she answered far more gravely. 'We enjoyed the same things!'

'Such as?'

'You're not serious?' she said, swinging to face him. 'Because I'm certainly not going to tell you.'

'At least tell me about what sort of work you do?'

She turned her pale, shining head back. 'My one talent is drawing. I've always been good at it and I trained for three years as a commercial artist. I've illustrated seven children's stories—a series of them by the same author.'

'Ever find yourself drawing your own face?' he asked.

The question seemed to amuse him, but there was a good deal of truth in it. 'I've used myself as a model from time to time,' she confessed.

'You're lucky to be able to afford the best!'

'Thank you.'

'You like your work?' he asked.

'Love it!' Her lovely smile lit up her sometimes too serious face, highlighting the bone structure. 'Being in the outback will be a wonderful experience for me. I'm quite good at drawing animals.'

'We'll see if we can find you a camel or two. You won't run short of kangaroos and emus and donkeys, not to mention the cattle, and we have a whole collie family, Shaeki and Shilo and the new litter. If you're any good at drawing flowers and birds as well, we're all going to be vastly entertained.'

'I'm not sure if I hate you!' she said crossly.

'Now why?'

'You have a vast capacity for making me feel as though I'm standing at the edge of a precipice and you're trying to push me.'

'Is that all?' he drawled.

'I find *that* completely terrifying.'

'You're certainly an imaginative child! I'm very clear-headed myself.'

'Men and women think in a different way,' said Melanie.

'I hope mine's the much better way! It's odd you should say that all the same. See straight ahead, that great yellow-brown cloud? It's about forty, fifty miles off.'

'Yes, what is it?' She spoke excitedly because the cloud formation looked positively eerie.

'A dust storm!' he said, rather curtly.

'And that's bad?'

'It's almost ten thousand feet up and it's spread over a big area,' he said.

'Do we fly through it or around it or what?' Melanie asked.

His silver eyes narrowed, and a muscle pulled beside his mouth. 'I've flown through dust storms before, but I don't think you'd fancy flying blind. It's not a pleasant sensation.' As he was speaking he was altering their straight course, and the altimeter needle moved downwards. 'It looks bad. We might have to stop.'

'Where?' she asked a little wildly. In the middle of God knows what desolation?

'Don't panic, for God's sake! You're not in any danger. That dust storm has made up my mind for me. We'll put down at Coraki. It's not in my flight plan and it will put us back hours, perhaps overnight. I'll radio Coorrabin and let them know of the possible arrival time. It's been so hot and still lately I might have expected it.'

Jay said little to her as he took the plane into a turn; the nose dipped, then climbed, levelling out again in a north-easterly direction. 'What a damned nuisance!'

'If you wanted to go through it, I'm not all that frightened!'

'Then you should be! Pilots before today have

72

flown through them and come out on range level, or even worse, tree level!'

'Wouldn't your instruments guide you?' she asked.

He hesitated, then looked at her. 'There's always some other element—mechanical failure, human error, air currents. I had an experience once in the Cessna I'm not likely to forget, a few minutes of hell. I'm not having any fears struck into you. We'll play it safe and land. I can run a check with Ron, that's my manager. It won't be all wasted time.'

'It wouldn't have happened if you hadn't come to get me.'

'Wishing I was Dave?' He glanced at her and some faint expression in his face made her heart stop.

'What do you mean?'

'Nothing, camellia face.' He handled the controls more firmly. 'Coraki isn't as civilised as Coulta, Ron's on his own. His wife got fed up with his close communion with the bush and went back to the city. Ron came to the Inland twenty years ago to die—he had some chronic bronchial condition that he developed as a child—but instead of dying he took to the bush like a duck to water and he's never had another attack from that day. Don't ask *me* why, I'm no medical man— perhaps it was an allergy thing. Anyway, Ron's as fit and strong as a top stockman should be. The bush saved his life, and he's never forgotten. Carol went off hoping he'd be finished, but he wasn't finished at all, in fact he's happier without her once the first shock died down.'

'Perhaps he's one of those destined to survive,' Melanie commented.

'Survival takes a special kind of courage.'

'I know it!' she said quietly.

'Not a day's going to plan lately!'

'I think we can agree about that,' she said.

'You should smile more often,' he told her. 'It's irresistible!'

'It's never got me what I wanted!' she said, looking down at her locked hands.

'Oh, I thought it had, or almost!'

She frowned and shook her silver-gilt head. 'All right, forget it. I don't think you and I are very good for each other!'

'Any particular reason?' Jay asked.

'You may improve when I get to know you better.'

He glanced at her briefly, brilliant accusation flashing out of his eyes. 'You're not the helpless little chick I took you for!' he said dryly.

'Something funny has happened to me since I met you.'

'Oddly enough, you're not the only one!'

After that, the silences grew longer until they were within a few miles of Coraki's landing strip. The touch down was perfect, but no one came out to greet them. The bungalow too was deserted, fairly stark and dreary by Coultra's standards, though it could have been improved in ten minutes by a woman's hand.

'It's obvious Ron's not around,' said Jay, moving fast through the few rooms. 'He's gone out and taken the boys. Let's see if they've taken the horses or the Toyota. You can wait here if you like.'

'No, I'll come with you.' The isolation of the bungalow was too much for her, the uncanny silence.

74

The four-wheel drive was parked in the gloom of one of the sheds, the keys in it, because who was there to take it? 'Climb in. We'll go for a ride.' Jay held out his hand and Melanie accepted it, feeling most unlike her old self. His air of command was so palpable she would have gone on a long trek with him anywhere. He might think her romance with his brother ridiculous and dangerous, but so too was her reaction to him.

Once in the Toyota he switched on the ignition and reversed the sturdy vehicle out of the shed, wheeling it round and starting off along the wide track that led away from the bungalow. The sun cast a fiery glow all over the ground, but the trees were beautiful, afire with coloured birds. Unlike the arid wastes they had flown over, this country was well covered with trees and vegetation but no sign of human life.

'Where *is* everyone?' she asked.

'Count *everyone* as five—Ron and four stockboys, three of them coloured. They could be anywhere. There's plenty to keep them occupied—mending fences and gates, searching out strays. It's obvious they're miles from here, but they'll turn up sooner or later. We'll go back to the house and radio Coorrabin. They'll know about the dust storm, but I'll radio them in any case. Now, this is where you begin to show your worth,' he went on. 'Think you can find us something to eat? Coffee won't keep a strong man going. Ron lives on beef and fish, but there should be plenty of tinned stuff. Carol had a vegetable garden at one stage. It was pretty impressive.'

'Poor Carol!' said Melanie softly.

'Yes,' he said briefly. 'I liked her. If you're lucky

you make it. The life was too lonely for her and she became very bitter.'

About a hundred yards in front of them, a huge red kangaroo suddenly hurtled out of the bushes and on to the track, pausing to stare at the approaching vehicle, propped up on its bipedal stance.

'*Get going!*' Jay sounded the horn and jammed on the brakes, swearing under his breath. 'See if there's not another one!'

There was—a smaller animal of a duller coat, its joey peering out of the carry-cot, its mother's pouch and the joey's home for seven or eight months. Their expressions were so curious and benign, Melanie laughed. 'How lovely!'

'You wouldn't laugh if they'd gone through the windscreen. It's happened before today. They have no road sense at all!' He blared the horn again and the kangaroos bounced off to the other side of the track, still pausing to look back at them. 'You can see now the reason for the kangaroo guards. They're a real menace, especially at night. Headlights just fascinate them. If you run into one it can do an awful amount of damage. Drivers have even been killed. They seem to get a death wish when a vehicle approaches hurtling right out in front of it.'

'My first kangaroo!' Melanie was still smiling, her expression gentle.

'You'll be seeing plenty of them,' Jay promised, his eyes on her profile. 'I'm sure you saw buffalo coming out of Darwin and if you'd stayed longer you could have found yourself a crocodile.'

'How entertaining!'

'The breeze has whipped up some colour in your cheeks,' he said suddenly. 'You were very pale.'

'I feel reborn!' she smiled. 'The air is like wine. A very dry one, and potent!'

'The outback might be your undoing,' Jay told her. 'Others can turn their backs on it, but I never could. You'll be lost if you let it establish its hold.'

Entranced, she gazed steadily at the bush scene around her. 'I love it, but I can quite see how the isolation might become frightening to a woman.'

'The life doesn't suit everybody. It has drawbacks, isolation and loneliness. One must have a deep abiding love for the land and some inner resources as well.'

'And you have!' It wasn't a question but a statement.

'It would seem so,' he agreed. 'The MacCallisters have been landowners for centuries. My great-great-grandfather was the younger son of a Scottish laird. The laws of primogeniture urged him out to Australia, along with a sense of adventure. He had the mind to lay claim to broad acres of his own, which of course he did, beyond anything he dreamed of. It was quite a race in those days and the scions of the Scottish lairds were there in the front ranks. The Outback is peppered with time-honoured names, Irish and English and Scotch!'

'So now I know what you remind me of!' Melanie mused.

'Oh?' He glanced at her sidelong, his brilliant eyes glinting.

'A Highland chieftain!'

'No!'

'Don't let it turn your head!' she smiled. 'I can see you in full regalia, velvet and tartan, white lace at the throat and wrists, a gorgeous silver brooch holding the plaid.'

'It just so happens, Melanie,' he said dryly, 'there's a portrait of the first MacCallister of Coorrabin in just such a costume. Also a portrait of my redoubtable great-great-grandmother, an unlikely-looking prototype of a pioneer woman with her blonde ringlets and eighteen-inch waist. Used to luxury all her life, she was never heard to complain of the life that confronted her after her marriage. Her courage and fortitude were outstanding, she was mistress of the vast solitude. You may find it of interest to read her journals—she kept them all her life. For a gently born English girl she understood perfectly the wild bush, even when it claimed the young brother who came out from England to visit her. It was a pretty horrifying story and I won't tell it to you.'

'It's shame to waste it!' said Melanie.

'I said no,' he repeated.

'Do you always say just what you mean?'

'I haven't the time to learn another style.'

She took a prudent look out of the window. A parrot of priceless beauty flew with a weird cry into the scented acacias. She pointed her hand at the spectacular bird, but it was gone. 'I didn't imagine those colours, did I?'

'The Princess Alexandra parrot, named after the then Princess of Wales. It's very beautiful with its flashing opal colours. They were commonplace once, but they're becoming rarer. If you're after bird life you're going to the right place. We have millions of them on Coorrabin—gigantic flocks of corellas and budgerigars and galahs, the variegated wrens and crimson chats, the finch and the quail. There are pelicans colonies in the remote swamps, huge flocks of ibis, spoonbills and herons and egrets, waterfowl galore, black swans. The Channel Country is a major breeding ground. When the rivers come down in flood the air is thick with them. The whistling tree ducks have even been known to mistake a glinting tin roof for a billabong by moonlight and crash on the roof in their hundreds. A lot of people can tell you that story and give imitations of the birds' startled cries!'

By now they were almost back at the bungalow. 'Let yourself go with the lunch,' Jay said with emphasis. 'I'll take a look around. There was a steer out there in the wrong place. I'll check it hasn't got caught up in the barbed wire.'

He let her down at the front stairs, then swung the Toyota around. 'I'll be five minutes. Think you can make out?'

'If I can't, I won't admit it!'

'What else might I expect?' he sighed.

Melanie waved him away, running lightly up the few stairs. Her eyes everywhere, and her ears constantly listening, she walked through to the small kitchen going through the row of cupboards. A great shiny beetle flew out of one, causing a minor alarm. She watched it zoom across the room, then she turned back to examining the contents. Tins of everything—soups, baked beans, spaghetti, jams, canisters of sugar, salt and flour, cooking and salad oils in large plastic bottles, vinegar, pickles and all the usual sauces, a colander full of new-looking potatoes, four large tins of Keen's mustard, neatly stacked in a row. The cupboards right of the sink held surprisingly good crockery, cutlery in the drawers beneath. The refrigerator, too, was well stocked: eggs, milk, cream, home-made butter, a leg of ham, several huge slices of steak, a large jar of honey, another of a vegetable extract, some kind of home-made bread wrapped in a tea-towel, vegetables that could only have been home-grown in the crispers. Carol's vegetable garden must have survived even if her marriage had failed. Life was a round of little ironies.

Curious now, Melanie opened the back door and walked out into what was almost a backyard farm. It gave her enormous satisfaction just to look at it. The flowerbeds had been left to their own devices, but the vegetable garden continued to be carefully tended, the soil newly turned over, the flourishing produce protected from the birds by a fine mesh canopy as tall as a man. All along the line of the back fence, fruit trees acted as a wind-break. She lifted the flap of the canopy to inspect the luxuriant rows of loose-head lettuce, the staked ripe and beautiful tomatoes, the cabbage and silver beet, the beans and the peas with carrots growing happily at their feet, the radishes and cucumbers and peppers, the leeks and the onions, round golden melons ripening in the sun, pumpkins and potatoes in abundance, parsley and mint confined by thick borders of marigolds. No one in their right mind could have left such a garden to go to seed. It was beautiful and it was responsive to all the glorious sunlight. It seemed to tell her such a lot about Carol. Poor Carol!

Two trips found Melanie back in the kitchen tossing up a salad. Ron would have to forgive her if she cut into his ham. She didn't fancy one of those enormous steaks, though she could see it was excellent quality beef. A few minutes more and she had found plastic place mats, wiped them over and set the table. The salad dressing only took seconds, the classic French recipe, but she left that to pour over the salad at the very last moment. Mustard she mixed in a small jug with a little of the vinegar.

Preparing a meal always gave her satisfaction. Her mother had been a wonderful cook. Sybil was good too, but in a less adventurous fashion. There was a lot to admire about Sybil, but it was heaven to be thousands of miles from her. Her father she missed, like a constant ache under her heart, but there was no use crying about it. She had promised him one thing, to let him know immediately she wanted to come home. Now Jay MacCallister had tried to extract from her almost the same promise. Did neither of them trust David? Was there some flaw in him she had missed?

The sound of the Toyota braking into the yard brought her back to the present. She turned around quickly and surveyed the table. Everything was ready and no cause for complaint. It was only left to her to pour the dressing over the salad. She could hear Jay's footsteps on the wooden boards of the verandah; but a few seconds more and he still hadn't come through to the kitchen nor called out. Melanie's forehead pleated and she walked back through the house herself.

'Jay, where are you?' she called.

'Trying to find myself a shirt. I've ripped my arm on

that blasted barbed wire. The steer was all tangled up in it and mad with fright. It's a wonder I didn't get a good swift kick in the head. Nothing's too tame around here!'

She came up short at the bedroom door, her face paling at the spectacle he presented.

'Don't you dare faint!' he said sternly.

'There's blood all over the place!' she gasped.

'Don't let it upset you. It looks a lot worse than it is. I've had my tetanus shots. Go away until I fix myself up.'

'Oh no! Let me help you. What are you looking for, another shirt?'

'Anything will do. This is a write-off!'

She came to stand beside him, looking down at the opened drawer and its modest contents. 'Ron doesn't seem to run to your kind of shirts.'

'I said *anything*!'

'All right, then, what about this?' She pulled out a faded blue denim. 'It's not even your size.'

'And what would you be knowing about that, Miss Kent?' He grabbed it, ripping off his own shirt, the muscles of his long darkly tanned back rippling. He was in perfect condition, very lean and hard. 'What's wrong with you?' he broke off to look at her slightly fazed face.

'Oh, nothing really. It's just your accident!' That and his half naked perfection, she thought, subject to a highly nervous reaction.

His dark face relaxed into a grin. 'If you must help me there's a medical kit in the bathroom.'

'I'll find it and clean up that wound.' A jagged gash

ran from his shoulder to his elbow, but Melanie kept her eyes off it. Jay MacCallister was pure dynamite, especially in a small room.

Ron's first aid kit was a comprehensive one. She took out scissors and a suitable roll of bandage and placed them beside the antiseptic and a few cottonwool swabs, covering her confusion with a show of efficiency.

Jay had come to the door, his eyes sweeping over her. 'Sure you're up to it?'

She shook her head slightly to clear it. Neither David nor anyone else had ever shocked her into this burning awareness. Her heart was beating erratically, but she turned around to face him. 'I do know how to tie a bandage.'

'Then why look like a little probationer in torment?'

'I'm never certain what you mean. But come along,' she said briskly, 'this won't hurt you!'

Jay laughed under his breath and walked over to the basin. 'Oh, I'm used to all sorts of things happening to me, Melanie.'

Energetically she filled the basin and tipped in a liberal quantity of antiseptic, a prickle of excitement making her fingers tremble. Jay MacCallister was a plain blasted nuisance. But most women would suffer the same reaction, she imagined, and immediately felt a little better. She had known there was some highly explosive element about him directly she had met him, but recognition had not provided her with the necessary immunity. There was a terrible magnetic strength about him that required a real fighting effort. She gritted her teeth and set about swabbing down the long gash. As she wiped fresh blood spurted and this made her get control of herself. 'It looks really bad, Jay,' she said.

'I don't think so. Here, give me that. You're too soft to be a good nurse!'

'I won't accept that!' She put the swab behind her back. 'Please let me finish.'

'It seems a pity when you're so pale.'

'You can't imagine how you look!' Her green eyes were huge and a pulse beat in the hollow of her throat.

'Nor you!' he said abruptly. 'All right, rinse it off and let's bandage it up.'

Melanie's small white teeth bit into her lower lip. She concentrated on the job as best she could, her eyelashes downcast as though she could avoid seeing the effect of the sunlight on his teak polished skin. Fool that she was! This was Jay, not David, but it required great effort to uproot her awareness of the wrong brother. Jay too seemed to be relieved when she was finished, twisting his lean frame away from her.

'That's pretty good, Melanie!' he drawled.

'I saw it once in a movie,' she explained.

'I must have missed that one.'

'Just as well!' she burst out like a fool. Awareness of him was reeling around in her brain. 'Oh, go away and put your shirt on!'

He laughed outright. 'Don't panic, little one. I'm on your side!'

'Are you?'

He turned back, his eyes flicking over her. 'Yes, and you'd better be pretty damned glad.'

'I'm learning that. When you're ready, I have lunch on the table.'

'I'd better call in Coorrabin first. There's something a little odd going on around here.'

Her face displayed her agreement, but it was obvious he meant some other way. 'I think that gash is shattering enough,' she said.

'Forget *that*! It's Coraki I'm talking about. Different things tell me messages.' His sparkling gaze had slipped away from her, the line of his jaw hardening. 'Come through to the radio room.' He caught up Ron's shirt and shouldered into it without wincing.

Some people could look good in anything, she thought. Why should she be so astonished by a faded old blue denim shirt that was too short in the arms for him? She turned away firmly. 'Shall we be speaking to David?' she asked.

'Do you want to?'

'Of course!' She controlled a shiver. *Of course* she wanted to speak to David, but her green eyes told him in a split second of her odd unwillingness. Perhaps she was nervous? Anyone could understand that. It would all be different when she heard David's voice. David was responsible for getting her out to Australia. She walked beside Jay, barely coming up to his shoulder.

'Cold feet can happen to anyone,' he said, allowing her to precede him into the small room.

'Does it show?' Melanie asked anxiously.

'That you're nervous, yes. So for that matter is Dave. Don't worry, Melanie, everything will turn out all right!'

That it wouldn't showed immediately. The voice that

came in from Coorrabin was David's, crackling with a kind of bitter anxiety.

'What the hell's going on, Jay? How long are you going to be there?'

Jay flicked a switch, his dark face expressionless. 'As long as it takes. Not a lifetime, certainly. You know about the dust storm?'

David spluttered in. 'So what? You've come through 'em before. To hell with the dust storm.'

His anger and antagonism was sticking out a mile. Melanie swallowed, listening to the conversation that passed to and fro, not looking at Jay. David was spitting out more wrath, and she rested her face in her hands, her elbows propped up against the long desk. Jay was saying he'd never come through a dust storm with a woman passenger, paying no attention to either Melanie nor his brother's outburst, pressing on with more important matters.

'Has Ron called in?' demanded Jay.

'Who cares?' snapped David.

'If I was there at this minute, you *would*!'

David seemed to quieten abruptly. 'He called in earlier this morning. There's been some trouble with one of the boys—Spider, I think. I wasn't paying a great deal of attention. Some fool tribal thing. He's on the run, scared out of his silly wits about something. Ron's gone after him.'

'Any talk of the local council stepping in?'

'How the hell would I know. Where's Melanie?'

Jay flicked his switch again. 'You can talk to her presently. If a camp council is involved it would explain

86

one or two things. Someone's been around the bunga-low—there are signs.'

There was a change in David, an undertone of inter-est. 'The rest of the boys will take to their heels. You know what they're like.'

'They already have. If Ron doesn't find Spider—God knows I wish you'd *listen*—his own people will. Apart from possible punishments we'll be a few men short. None of the other boys will come back. I'll stay here until Ron gets back.'

'You'll what?'

Jay cut his brother off and beckoned Melanie to the transceiver. She sat down in the swivel chair, then David was on the air again, his voice urgent and posses-sive. 'Melanie?'

'Here, David. I'm so sorry about your arm.'

David brushed that aside, feeling he owed her none of the usual courtesies. 'I want you to come straight on here now,' he ordered her. 'Do you hear?'

'I can't do that without Jay.' She looked up into Jay's sardonic face, holding his scrutiny.

'You damned well can!' David protested. 'You get him to bring you in here. You can make him. You haven't come all the way from England to get stuck up at Coraki with Jay. Blast Ron and his troubles!'

Jay flicked the switch and Melanie answered as reasonably as she could. 'I'm sorry you're upset, David, but the dust storm looked bad. I didn't really want to fly through it. I'm not used to light aircraft and I'm sure Jay knows what he's doing!'

This was the red rag to the bull. 'Are you siding with him already?'

'David, you're shouting!'

'Why shouldn't she?' Jay took over. 'Staying alive is important!'

'I'll kill you, Jay!'

'That'll be the day!' Jay said in a brutally firm tone.

Melanie withdrew quickly. She was, she realised, shocked. She had risked a good deal coming to Australia. David had sounded quite different—violent and jealous, riding a wave of fury. Her slender body was trembling weakly. Not even in her wildest imaginings would David have behaved like that. He had been so kind and considerate. But just then on the radio he had sounded goaded beyond measure. Disappointment, impatience, was permissible, but not that harsh possessiveness, the fear of his brother. She wasn't his wife, nor yet his fiancée, and she would have objected to his manner had she been either. Jay was still talking, his voice curt, clearly giving orders that he expected to be carried out. Finally he switched off the radio and came through to the other room to her.

'I'm sorry about that,' he said.

She shrugged weakly. 'Why was he so angry?'

'David gets angry about a lot of things.'

'I don't believe it!'

'Maybe not yet.'

She twisted her blonde head away. 'He hasn't with me.'

'Not up to date! Don't make too much of it. He'll be over his emotional disturbance by the time we get back.'

'So we're staying?'

'We *have* to. I don't intend this thing to get out of hand.'

'What sort of thing?' asked Melanie wearily. 'You've told me nothing.'

'You couldn't understand it fully, if I did. Come along, let's have lunch.'

'I don't want any.'

His hand dropped to her shoulder, compelling her through to the kitchen. 'Little girls are not allowed to argue,' he said firmly.

'So it seems,' she sighed. 'This might turn out to be a very difficult trip.'

'You wanted to come. Don't give in yet.'

'Surely that would please you, as you're obviously the man in charge.'

'Now, Melanie!' his silver eyes mocked her. 'You've prepared a nice lunch. Let's not spoil it with our first tiff.'

'Are you ever serious?' she said dryly.

'Do you want me to be serious?' He stopped suddenly and looked down at her silky head.

'Why, yes, you're important to my survival!'

'So you know that already?'

'You know perfectly well what I mean!' she said, disconcerted, the colour staining her cheekbones.

'In this case we're here on Coraki. By accident.'

'I know, and I find it amusing.'

'Good. Time enough later to go to the pack. Here, take this. We'll have lunch on the verandah. I find Ron's little kitchen too damned cramped and you watching me like an unwinking kitten, green eyes glowing.

You're not restful, Melanie, and I thought that you were!'

If it wasn't amused mockery, she didn't know what it was. She took the plates and the knives and forks and he waved her away like she was another one of his employees. She made another trip and somehow they were seated out on the verandah, protected from the brilliant sunshine by the deep overhang. It was quite true; she felt an entirely different girl from the one she had been only a few days ago. She gave Jay a swift oblique look, only to find him watching her.

'Why don't you start? Being a gentleman, *I* can't until you pick up your knife and fork.'

'A reply occurs to me,' snapped Melanie.

'Don't say it. Didn't you make any mustard?'

'Yes, I did.' As if caught out on the most common-place chore she went to jump to her feet, but Jay shot out his hand, locking her wrist.

'I'll get it,' he said.

'Why are you smiling?' she asked.

'Well, you don't want me to be serious!' His grey eyes lit his dark face, almost bemusing her. Even his going through to the kitchen gave her a breathing space. With her feet digging into the floorboards she still felt uprooted. When he came back she asked him to explain about Spider. It was another world out here, but she did want to understand it.

'Spider, if it *is* Spider, and it sounds like him, is a fully initiated member of his tribe. From what I can make out he's transgressed some tribal law. It could be a breach against sacred law, or an offence against a person. Maybe one of the women. Short of murder he can be turned over to the tribe for punishment. The ritual leaders take action. They meet secretly and decide on an appropriate punishment. One or more of them might carry it out. In this case, I think there's only one man involved—the Red Ochre Man or his equivalent.'

'I don't believe this!' Melanie said, looking around almost furtively.

'This is Coraki, not Piccadilly Circus. That's the trouble with you city-bred girls.'

'And this Red Ochre Man is after Spider?'

'It would seem so. Eat up like a good girl. This salad is brilliant, though it could have done with just a trace of garlic. I should have told you where to find it.'

'I wish you'd just tell me about Spider,' Melanie persisted.

'I don't want to frighten you.'

'Why should you frighten me?'

His glance sharpened over her fragile femininity, her wide, startled eyes. 'Let's say, little one, if the offence was against sacred law Spider can expect the death penalty. I don't know what all this is about, but it's not going to break out into open violence. The presence of the Red Ochre Man in the vicinity would frighten the daylights out of the coloured boys.'

'I should think so. What is he, a witch doctor?'

'He's the man elected by the camp council to carry out whatever punishment is deemed necessary. I just hope it's a woman.'

'Isn't a woman sacred enough?' she asked, her voice fraught with censure.

'Woman magic hasn't any supernatural basis, though

enough feuds over women break out. Sacred law involves regulations, tabus, that kind of thing. Violations of the strict tribal codes of behaviour.'

'Now you're frightening me!' she said, putting her fork down.

He was silent for a moment watching her, then he spoke very briskly. 'No violence will ever be intended towards me or any member of my household. That includes you. It's Spider I have to look out for, even though he seems to have laid himself open to some kind of reprisal. These councils are scrupulously fair. One thing's certain, he's gone for the lick of his life and the other boys with him. Ron had better give up the chase and come home. God, they're all twenty-four-hour days lately!'

'And I'm an additional burden!'

'Now how could you ever imagine that? You're as beautiful as a waterhole in the desert, you can fix a nice meal and tie up a bandage. What more could a man want?'

'I can't shoot and hunt and cut cattle like—what was her name?'

'Hilary. That's quite true. Still, there's no point in comparing the two of you. If it makes you any happier I'd rather be stuck here with you. Hilary, for all her assets, can wear rather thin.'

'No doubt I will in time. What are you going to do about all this?'

'Are we back to Spider?'

'You know I am!'

'Just as I was beginning to enjoy your company!' There was a devastating twist to his mouth, but he began to speak seriously again. 'If I stay here I can try to settle the dispute. I've an idea the court of law is somewhere in the vicinity.'

'Isn't that dangerous?' she queried.

'It's part of my job. No, I don't think there's any danger. They'll have spotted the plane. They all know it's mine.'

'Who are *they*?'

'Pay attention, Melanie. *They* are the ones who want to settle the grievance in their own way. If it's very serious it has to be settled the white man's way. Spider is on the payroll. Most of the time Ron is a substitute for MacCallister. It so happens I'm here now. Let them speak to me.'

'What it all adds up to is you're the MacCallister, the local laird.'

'A pity there wasn't some reference to me in Dave's letters.'

Melanie looked directly into a pair of eyes that sparkled with mockery. She was convinced he could read her mind, but she cut in on him smoothly enough:

'How do you know there wasn't?'

'The first time you saw me you looked as if you were about to slash me to ribbons—more my fault than Dave's that he hadn't mentioned me, for whatever his reasons.'

'Well, I know all about you now.'

'Ah, and you're not happy.'

'You mustn't mind!'

'The woods are full of pretty girls, Melanie.'

'I can see that they might be. Are you considering honouring any one of them at all?'

'One marriage at a time. No, don't flutter!' He caught the tips of her fingers. 'Make me a cup of coffee.'

'*Please!*' she said pointedly.

'You don't say please, why should I?'

'You're a very complicated man, Jay MacCallister, and I'm going to catch fire if I stay here.'

'Now what kind of an admission is that?'

She rose quickly and walked away to the kitchen with his empty plate, declining to answer. He excelled at that sort of talk. She couldn't match him, yet oddly she felt exhilarated, as much as she was annoyed. Jay MacCallister was *too* attractive. Probably it was common knowledge that he could charm the birds from the trees. He was equally not to be taken seriously. For all his remarkable eligibility he was in no hurry to change his bachelor status. Women were playthings and she didn't play that kind of game. Besides, there was David. No denying, incredibly, his image had dimmed and the line he had taken on the radio had antagonised and upset her. Had her feeling for him been a temporary state, an emotional by-product of her unhappy home situation? She wouldn't really know until she was with him again on Coorrabin. At this point a wave of perplexity came over her. Could all the wanting and needing mean nothing? It was odd, extremely odd. She leant against the sink, her head bent.

'Melanie?'

'Yes?' She didn't want to turn to him.

'Do you actually want to cry or to make the coffee?'

'You're a slavedriver, Jay,' she grumbled.

'Turn around,' he ordered.

'No, I won't!'

'Have it your own way. I'm just going over to the sheds again.'

'Then I'm coming with you. You're not going to leave me to any Red Ochre Man.'

'Or any other man. Come along, then. I can make the coffee later. You're all shot to pieces!'

She had the option of denying it violently or going with him. She met that brilliant speculative gaze and went quietly.

CHAPTER FIVE

DARKNESS descended with little warning. One moment the sky was one of the world's wonders, a great crimson vault, shafted with pink and gold, coloured parrots and water fowl streaking through it on their way to the swamps, then a brief transition period when the bush turned to a misty, indistinct mauve, then frightening, complete blackness, a world changed beyond recognition, deprived of all source of light. It made Melanie nervous, though she tried hard to hide it.

About an hour later, the stars came out—not stealthily, taking their place one by one in the ghostly dark, but altogether, as at the flick of a switch, a pulsing dazzle of light, blazing thickly along the curve of the Milky Way, studding the points of the Southern Cross. She had never seen such stars before nor witnessed a sun that set in such a red and gold glory. In a way she could not explain, she felt herself changing. This was

95

another world, urgent, a fantasy world, harsh and beautiful and demanding. Feelings were surfacing in her, washed up in waves, feelings she had never suspected she possessed. This was a new Melanie, and she had started out on a journey that perhaps she should never have made.

David had written her that he could not do without her. Then there was Jay. She couldn't explain him at all, or his effect on her. She felt innocent and ignorant beside him, one minute brittle with tension, the next buoyant, weightless, exhilarated as she had never been in her life. It was enough to convince her she didn't love David. She was finished almost before she had started. Why wasn't David beside her chasing away the currents his brother had set in motion? She closed her eyes and rested her forehead against the timber support of the verandah. The stars glittered down on her, wondering if she had gone to sleep.

Somehow Jay materialised beside her, his lean hands grasping the rail. 'I wonder if this day's ever going to end?'

Melanie lifted her blonde head, her skin in the shadowed light with the translucence of a pearl. 'We're miles and miles into nowhere.'

'I suppose that's very important to a woman,' he observed.

'I'm no stranger to loneliness.'

'Well, you *should* be!' he said almost curtly. 'Why have you tied your hair back like that?'

'The heat, I suppose!' she said untruthfully. She had deliberately tried to make herself look plainer, but her eyes shone like green fire.

His mouth twisted fractionally. 'What's the matter?'

'I wish I knew,' she sighed.

He lifted his hand abruptly and caught at the silk square that tied back her hair at the nape. 'Don't bother with that! Hair like yours should swing free!'

'What about when it gets in my eyes?' Her own hand went up distractedly to smooth back the silky forward sweep on to her face.

'Leave it!'

She stared at him as if he could shape her to his own designs. 'It's so strange,' she said, 'but I feel thousands and thousands of miles from everything that's familiar to me.'

'Anything you want to know, ask!'

'*Ask!*' she repeated in a soft, forlorn voice, turning her sensitive face up to the night sky. 'All right, Jay, why are the stars so big and brilliant, as if every light in the world has been turned on? It makes up for the dark of an hour ago, the primeval silence!'

'You'll get used to it!' he said crisply, his eyes on her profile.

'If I stay!'

'And why won't you?' The question was gentle yet relentless.

She didn't answer directly. 'Thank heaven you're here. I think I'd go mad if I was on my own.'

'It happened to Carol,' he said hardly.

'And it's decided you about me.'

'A lot of women would feel the same.'

She twisted away, the light caught in her hair. 'I don't think Ron's coming back,' she said.

'It's early yet. He might.'

'I feel as if someone's watching me.'

'*I* am!'

'Probably that's the reason I'm so nervous!'

'Morning can't come soon enough!' said Jay, his voice mocking.

'I feel safe with you, Jay,' she confessed.

'Do you?'

'Shouldn't I?'

'Why not? I might believe you if you turned your face this way. I swear I intended none of this.'

'I'm *not* alarmed!' she said, looking back at him finally, her voice despite all her efforts sounding breathless, racing.

'No, merely trembling!'

'Don't taunt me, Jay,' she begged.

'I've got to keep busy some way!'

He half smiled, and she could see the curve of his chiselled mouth. His ability to make her heart knock madly against her narrow ribs she no longer questioned. She could never see him as David's brother, or a possible brother-in-law, but a strongly individual man, with reference to nobody but himself. How he saw her she didn't know. A rather nervous and imaginative English girl, perhaps? His brother's future wife? Someone unattainable. They were within arm's reach of one another. She dragged her eyes off him, unable to relax. He was studying her as much as she was studying him —maybe more.

'We'd better have a drink!' he said in his completely self-assured fashion.

'I don't want it,' said Melanie.

'Why not?'

'I might start acting noticeably different.'

'Oh, in what way?'

'We might start quarrelling!'

Jay shrugged his shoulders, his white smile reappearing. 'I *had* noticed the electricity crackling!'

'Well, you're studying me pretty closely.'

'And you me!'

Melanie couldn't look away from those light, seeking eyes. Outwardly they were acting under some form of restraint, but something existed in their senses, linking them together whether they liked it or not. It couldn't have been an illusion in her own mind, because his eyes had narrowed to diamond slits, speculative, faintly hostile, as if he resented her femininity and the sensuous current of awareness it inspired.

'I'm going to fetch you a drink, Melanie,' he said briefly. 'We're going to quarrel anyway. Sip it if you have to, I'll add plenty of soda. All right there by yourself for a minute?'

'Perfectly. Shouldn't you call David again?'

He turned back to glance at her, the light palpitating in her long blonde hair. 'Think we ought to risk it?'

'I've an idea you'd risk anything.'

'Now I *am* going!' he said curtly, his dark face inscrutable.

'Oh, Jay!' Despite herself it came out as a plea.

'Well?'

'I don't mean anything,' she stammered. 'Forgive me, I'm a bit nervous. You don't think we're going to have any visitors, do you?'

'A raiding party?' he asked crisply.

'Yes.'

'I'm here, Melanie. I don't run. There's nothing to fear.'

'What about your arm?' Anxiety and fatigue made her eyes huge, intensely green in her pale face. For a moment she thought he wasn't going to waste his breath on replying.

'Don't fuss!' He looked back at her, his expression faintly impatient. 'I mend easily!'

'See what's happening at Coorrabin.'

'Is that an order?'

'I wouldn't dare give you one.'

'Oddly enough I don't give a damn what's happening at home,' said Jay.

'I thought it was more important to you than anything?'

'That's just what I thought!'

'Look ...' she began.

'Shut up,' he said briskly. 'We're left with no alternative but to split up. If you're hungry we can have something to eat as well. It's your department—that, and the half smiles and the green eyes.'

She felt shaky with a too bright antagonism. 'I'm not entirely dependent on you, Jay MacCallister!'

'Yes, you are.'

'And you like it?' she accused him.

'*Sure!*'

He walked inside, leaving her breathing quickly. What kind of a set-up did they have now? One word in the wrong place would make all the difference. It was insane, but she knew she couldn't handle him. Something about him undermined her composure, incited the sharpest, most incomprehensible yearnings.

100

She would have to go very, very carefully, for it seemed to her now they had a decidedly odd effect on one another, as if each was waiting for the other to make the first move. Melanie couldn't deny it or reconcile it with anything in her past experience. It wasn't at all like that with David. David had accepted the gentle yoke she had placed on him without question, marvelling at her discipline and principles. If she truly loved David, his image would cling to her with brilliant persistence, instead of fading without a murmur. She winced at her own inconsistency and covered her face with her hands. The night scents were all around her, unfamiliar and heady, quickening every pulse in her body. A hand touched her shoulder and she cried out, a sweet, plaintive sound, young and endangered.

'You'd better come inside!' Jay said tersely. 'Is there any need to jump out of your skin when I touch you?'

'I'm not too proud to say you frightened me.'

'*Past* tense?'

'I'm coming!' Melanie took the glass out of his hand and walked past him, her eyes a green blaze and colour in her cheeks. Jay followed her with infinite slowness so that she had already sunk down into the old leather sofa, nursing her drink between her hands.

'What *is* this?' he asked, his voice almost angry, 'fright at first sight?'

She seemed to droop, her delicate shoulders turning inwards. 'I'm doing my best to remain calm. What is it you expect of me, Jay?'

'Not that idiotic little cry!' he snapped.

'Why is it making you so damned angry? You said

you were used to all sorts of things happening to you.'

'It might have been simpler to go through that dust storm.'

'I'd want to now, but we *can't*!' She was almost shouting, sick and startled at the deep temper she was showing. She hadn't even known she possessed just such a temper. She could hurl something at him, he looked so contemptuous his silver eyes sparkling, filling her with this unbearable, waiting excitement.

'When I first saw you,' he said slowly, 'I thought you were a girl of considerable restraint, but there's all sorts of depths to you.'

'I'm sure no one else has told me!'

'Perhaps no one else has rocked the boat. You don't know yourself at all.'

'You're right about that!' she said with something of his own curtness.

He stood up, very tall, very dark, and she could feel her nerve shrivelling. There was no vestige of good will between them, no reassurance, no studied appropriate courtesies, but a naked current of tension. He had a very arrogant look about him, she could see that now, a high-mettled look that justified her apprehensions. Whatever he chose to do he would do. No woman could keep him on a tight leash. He was probably every bit as dangerous as he seemed at that minute, but there was no denying his attraction or her inability to defend herself against it.

He turned back to her and spoke briskly. 'Drink that, then we'll go a bit further to cheer you up.'

'You mean call David?'

'What else? Don't waste those glances on me. I'm

102

only the stand-in with a difficult job to do.'

'I can't speak to you, Jay!' she burst out almost in desperation. 'You were perfectly all right this afternoon.'

'Come, come,' he drawled reprovingly, 'surely you realise all your casual chatter has cut out as well?'

'Oh, have it your own way!' she said wearily. 'You can spend a lifetime acting one way, then you meet someone who makes you act like somebody else.'

'The trouble with you, little one, is you haven't lived at all. In fact, you're not qualified yet to be even thinking of marriage.'

'Oh, please speak frankly,' she said, staring at him with her green eyes.

'I thought I was. Now, let's get Dave on the air to reassure you of his undying devotion, then we'll have dinner for two.'

'Someone should have warned me about you,' Melanie said bitterly.

'I'm very sorry, Melanie,' he smiled at her, 'I didn't think it would be necessary!'

'It was necessary all right. There's a great deal to be said for a familiar face.'

He glanced down at her, his brilliant eyes mocking. 'Why, Melanie, we *were* introduced. I mean, aren't you overdoing the melodrama a bit?'

'You don't suggest moderation!'

'Moderation isn't the most important thing in the world. That might be where you went wrong with your little plan.'

'What plan?' she asked, falling into the trap.

Jay didn't answer for a moment, though his strange

eyes almost had her transfixed, taunting, speculative, a vertical frown between his black brows. 'Either you're an excellent actress, Melanie, or a bit dense. Why, to marry Dave, of course. Isn't that what you came out for?'

'I'd scorn such a plan!' she said heatedly, and the blood rushed under her flawless skin.

'Really? You must be quite different from the rest of your sex. A man can hardly walk around by himself without unwanted attentions!'

'You must be the only man alive to be depressed by that.'

'Oh, I can take it or leave it!' he said with a deep insolence, with eyes glittery with amusement. 'Come on, Melanie, let's use the time a little more profitably. Speak to Dave. Find your voice again and forget his remarks at your last effort.'

She swung to her feet and came to stand beside him, making herself look up at his dominant, dark face. 'You go in for a certain amount of violence yourself!'

'Nothing like that, camellia face. I'm treating you with great gentleness and respect. I mean, what else are brothers-in-law for?'

'Some of them are pretty grim!' she said recklessly, feeling her palm tingle.

'Keep that little hand where it is!' he said softly.

'This isn't the first time I've wanted to hit you and haven't!'

'Now who's violent?'

Her small face was brooding, a little bewildered by her own unprecedented reactions. 'I suppose one learns new things about oneself every day.'

'That's *right*, Melanie!'

Some vaguely caressing note in his voice made her shiver. 'You win again!' she said almost bitterly.

'That goes without saying. Admit it, Melanie, you actually like crossing swords with me.'

'Nothing of the sort,' she said emphatically, tossing the silky slide of hair back off her face. Where was that damned scarf?

'Let's call Dave in case that's not true.'

She could feel her face burning under his mocking gaze. 'Let's do it at once. You're blocking my way. You're too tall!'

'Anything else?'

'Yes, you've got the devil in you, not David!' She ducked quickly under his outstretched arm and went into the other room. Some men were just too frankly masculine. They threatened and challenged a woman at every turn. That kind of thing was all right if one wanted to live dangerously, but she didn't. She was very conventional, and Jay MacCallister wasn't. He was almost locking her into a dreadful excitement, making her regret the quickness of her tongue, the telling heat in her cheeks. She felt extraordinarily restive and she knew it showed in her face. The conviction nearly defeated her. Whatever her future she would have to keep a considerable distance from Jay MacCallister.

From the easy expression on his face he didn't appreciate or concern himself with her dilemma. He turned on the transmitter, calling in Coorrabin, leaning forward to flick a switch. The radio came alive, no crackle, no static, a voice similar to David's but younger, gayer. To her amazement Melanie saw Jay's face soften in a way that flustered her. She had become used to his hard, compelling brand of charm. His tenderness would be devastating.

The young engaging voice was bright and interested. 'Howdy, Boss, how's things?'

'Great! No harm's come to us at any rate. Where's Dave?'

'Prepare yourself. He's drunk or the like. Runnin' off with his girl!'

Jay grinned his wide, sensuous mouth turning down. 'What proof has he got of that?'

'The usual!' said Greg.

Jay cut him off. 'Here's your opportunity to speak to Melanie. She's here right now—a vision and no mistake!'

'Hello, Melanie, hello!' Greg was laughing.

'Hello, Greg. How are you? I'm looking forward to meeting you in the morning.'

'Me too. Gosh, do *you* sound nice! Don't you worry about anything now. Just you relax. Jay will look after you. I was only kidding.'

'Were you?' Melanie was back on the air again. 'He's carrying on in an intolerable fashion at the moment.'

Jay almost lifted her out of the chair, taking over. 'Thank you, Melanie. She's joking, of course, Greg. The English sense of humour!'

'I like it!' said Greg. 'By the way, Larry put down en route to Adelaide. He came through the dust storm and emerged with banana legs. Dot was nearly hysterical by the time we got her up to the house. She reckoned they even turned upside down like the birds.'

'Why the devil did he do that?'

'Can't say!' Greg's voice was laconic. 'You've flown through them yourself—but then Larry isn't in the same class.'

'I hope you told him,' drawled Jay.

'He just laughed—that's when we could get his hand unstuck from the controls. They had a pretty rough trip. Dot withdrew to the guest wing immediately. I think she's going to divorce him. Ron turn up yet?'

Jay's silvery eyes touched Melanie's face. She was standing beside him, leaning back against the desk. 'No,' he said briskly. 'Spider's relations are in the neighbourhood.'

'Sure of it?' Greg sounded anxious.

'I'm sure.' This hard and firm.

'Maybe they'll cut him up a bit?' Greg ventured.

'Maybe he deserves it. Anyway, I'm staying to hear both sides. Ron might camp overnight, but he'll come in by daylight at the latest. I'll let you know.'

'Let me speak to Melanie again,' Greg pleaded. 'Why should you have all the luck?'

'I'm the eldest.'

It was Greg again, laughing and groaning. 'Melanie, oh, Melanie, what a terrible day I've had! Dave acting up like a mad brumby, the Boss gone, me giving the decisions. Get home, girl, and settle us all down.'

'I'm hoping to as soon as possible, Greg!' she assured him.

'Don't let Jay rattle you,' he said kindly. 'He's a first-class clown.'

'I *have* thought so!'

'That's pretty shrewd! I expect he thinks you're terrific!'

'No, I don't think it's that!' said Melanie.

'Don't worry, he'd never admit it!'

'Goodnight, Greg!' Jay said firmly. 'I'll call in in the morning.'

'Enjoy yourselves!'

'Young idiot!' Jay turned the radio off. 'We haven't any party talk left.'

'I like the sound of Greg,' Melanie said warmly.

'He's doing very nicely,' Jay admitted. 'Probably the nicest of all of us.'

'*I* think so.'

He straightened up and stared at her. 'Melanie, Melanie, do you love Dave or not?'

'Unfortunately we can't love to order,' she sighed. 'Niceness hasn't much to do with it.'

'I should hope it would be a contributing factor. You and I seem to have vastly different ideas!' He slumped back in the swivel chair, easing his shoulders. 'What happens now, Miss Kent? Dinner à deux? Ron might be back by the time we finish it.'

'Do you really think that?'

'It's what you want to hear. My guess is he won't come in till morning. At your age you need a good night's sleep and you've been travelling for days. You'll go off like a new-born kitten.'

She shook her blonde head. 'Not so easy—the wild bush and suchlike.'

In the same instant a sound was borne on the night wind that almost froze the blood in her veins. 'What's that?' she asked shakily.

'I thought you'd never ask. Dingoes. It's quite natural. It's the way they talk to each other!'

'It's unearthly!' Melanie shuddered. 'They sound like wolves!'

'They *do* possess wolf-like characteristics. They howl instead of barking, they stalk their prey in the same way and they grate their teeth through ... oh, forget it. You'll have to get used to that sound, though I grant you it's pretty eerie!'

'And yet it belongs here in some special way!' Melanie said, managing to make it sound terrifying.

There was a moment's silence while he looked at her, his face serious, almost abstracted, then he clapped his hands together briskly as though reaching a decision. 'Come, come, Melanie, where would we be without mealtimes? Think you can cook a steak?'

'A steak?'

'As in barbecues,' he supplied dryly. 'What's wrong with you, anyway? Stars in your eyes?'

'Right, a steak!' she said, shrugging her shoulders, obviously trying to rouse herself. 'I know it's probably treason, but it's much too thick for me.'

'I can *cut* it, you finicky little creature. Anyway, you could do with a little meat on those chicken bones.'

'I'm the right weight for my height,' she told him. 'Maybe a bit under.'

'The first willy-willy will blow you away!' he said, at once.

'Don't underestimate me, Jay MacCallister!'

'Why, Melanie, I'm fighting not to go the other way. This thing between us, I'm sure, can be transformed into a close family friendship!'

She raised her green eyes to his face. 'The picture doesn't come easily to mind,' she said.

'Well, we're in a state of anticipation about something! You tell me.'

'I think it's more sensible to drop it.'

'Who's sensible, or reasonable, are you?'

'I know you like to see how people react,' said Melanie. 'Don't deny it.'

Jay stood up and pressed his hands over his eyes, almost wearily. 'There's nothing wrong with that in itself, Melanie. The best weapon against attack *is* attack!'

She shook her head. She could say nothing. Such confident authority was designed to leave her defenceless. He was right, of course—she was in a weird state of anticipation that was leaving her almost physically breathless. Either an event, or a person, or both. To lose herself in the preparation of another meal, cutting conversation to a minimum, seemed vital. She smiled and let her body ease as she walked past him, defeating her own impulse to run. Jay MacCallister had better appreciate that she could play a game of her own!

After that, and during the meal, he seemed to relent, teasing her gently much as he would his sister Susan. When he smiled, Melanie looked down, deeming it necessary like a brake on her. In vain had she looked for signs of David in him, something of David to cling to, but as Glory had pointed out, the brothers were quite different, beyond a superficial family resemblance. Surprisingly, she managed to eat most of her portion, but she couldn't put away the cold beer which was all Ron ran to plus a half bottle of Vat 69. Jay did most of the talking, though she asked questions from time to time: things about the station, his way of life, his family, their pioneer background. He was a very amusing and fluent talker, and Melanie began to lose the extreme nervousness of the earlier part of the evening, her green eyes dancing when he recounted a funny though nearly disastrous episode in the buffalo country outside Darwin, before he moved on to tales of Coorrabin's ghost, a spirit that haunted a particular waterhole on the run, and its effect sometimes comic, sometimes serious, on the family and different stockmen over the long years. Whether the stories were true or not, and she had no real reason to doubt him, they kept her on the edge of her seat, like a child at a pantomime. She was entirely bereft of any such experiences to offer herself.

While he talked, Jay watched her captive young face. Lovely as it was, it was yet very vulnerable. She didn't know her own mind at all, though in a way she was brave. It had taken courage to leave the father she obviously loved to come out to a new life in a much different world. Her introduction to it hadn't been easy. Risks were always being taken in the Outback, but she wasn't used to that way of life nor painted totem men with feathered slippers and sacred armbands lurking right outside her door. A necessary part of Jay's job was maintaining order. It compelled him to remain where he was, when his strong inclination had been to get her to Coorrabin as soon as possible. At the same time, if she was going to be initiated into their way of life, she might as well learn now.

She looked as fragile as a flower in the desert, the Carpet of Snow, with her shining hair, her eyelashes

111

cast down and a nerve beating at the base of her neck. Being a man, Jay couldn't ignore her beauty and its drawing power. It was subtle but very strong. He knew her effect on Dave and he knew the dangers for himself. He would have cursed his head off if it would have done him any good. At least she wasn't as nervous of him as she had been before dinner. Even the accidental meeting of their fingers had revealed her young agitation, though she tried hard to guard her green eyes, darkened in the night light to jade. It required quite an effort to treat her like Susan or one of Sue's friends, but he thought he was succeeding. Every movement she made was intensely graceful and feminine. It put his teeth on edge the way she twisted her body and put a hand to her hair. Oh, lord, it was going to be a very long night with just such a girl-child!

Casually he offered to help with the dishes. Melanie smiled but refused, and he was glad of it. It gave him a chance to preserve his own immunity. It seemed a pity she would make the worst possible sister-in-law— certainly for him. Women generally messed up the best laid plans and he made no effort to put the thought out of his mind. She would definitely interfere with everyone's work. Greg would fall in love with her on sight. He had never been exposed to such a tender young creature with her petal white skin and her mermaid colouring—great for the desert fringe and the long scorching summers. For his own peace of mind, he should shun her like the plague, but that was hardly possible. Women brought chaos, they always did. Thank God she was tired out. She should sleep for hours on end. He'd better make up some kind of bed

112

for himself—not the sofa; it was a good foot too short, he had discovered. The camp bed out on the verandah should do. He could find a few cushions. It was too hot for any kind of a covering.

A splintering crash, then a scream from the kitchen really did start him swearing. Swifter than she could ever have imagined a man could move, he was there, grimness hardening his mouth, consternation making daggers of his eyes :

'What the hell——?' he demanded.

Melanie looked on the point of tears, staring fixedly at the broken crockery. Jay moved towards her, catching her on the point of the shoulder, shaking her none too gently. 'Melanie? Surely you're not crying over a few broken dishes.'

'Oh, don't be so kind to me!' she moaned. 'I don't deserve it!'

'What *is* it?' He sounded frustrated.

'You're hurting me!'

'A lovely thought! I don't think I can stand all these female jitters!'

'It was a snake!' she said, shuddering. 'It came right in the back door.'

He kicked it shut with his foot. 'Little fool! Why did you open it?'

She looked back at him as if he had gone mad. 'It's so *hot*! How was I to know a snake intended to mount the back stairs?'

'There are snakes everywhere if you really look round,' he pointed out brutally.

'Oh!'

Melanie looked as if she was going to pass out, and

the thought raged angrily in his mind. With a sudden violence he pulled her towards him, his dark face formidable, impatient as all hell. 'For Pete's sake—you pass out or have hysterics and I'll smack you!'

This seemed to restore her sanity. 'There's something I have to tell you,' she said raggedly. 'You're a bully, and highly impatient!'

'Damn that! Come into the other room. Forget it, Melanie, though I suppose it was pretty ghastly.'

'I've never seen a snake in my life!' she said, her voice scarcely above a whisper, imploring him to understand. 'They're vile, simply vile. It's normal where I come from to have a horror of snakes, but now I see they're good friends of yours.'

'What colour was it?' he asked, still the barbarian.

'How should *I* know? Oh, brown, a dark greenish brown—I don't know. I turned around and it was there, stretching its full length, then it coiled up in a flash. I thought it was going to strike me.'

'You had something worse lined up for it, a couple of plates. I bet it moved out fast!'

'Oh, don't, *don't* bother about me. You're heartless,' she turned away. 'I'm going to bed, Jay. It's been a long day one way and the other. Does the door lock?'

'What the devil are you talking about?' He spun around, his silver eyes slashing.

'I said does the door lock?'

'How utterly charming! From me or the snake?'

'I don't need either of you as a chaperon.'

'Sit down here!' he said tautly, obviously unused to the slightest insult with his black, fiery pride.

'No, I *won't*!' she snapped. 'I've absolutely had it.

I've been trying to keep a stiff upper lip all day and the results are tragic. I feel like I'm going to pieces and I'd like to do it in private. The rotten thing was endless. I'm sure it was five or six feet!'

'That's a baby!'

A fierce, hot rush of anger blurred his words and his mocking dark face. Not all men were so diabolically masculine, strictly without comfort of any kind. She found a thick book under her hand and hurled it at him, with about eighty per cent accuracy.

Jay's reflexes were excellent. He caught it neatly and returned it to the table. 'I don't really appreciate that, Melanie!' he drawled.

'What do I care?' she snapped. 'I think it was justified!'

'Don't be ridiculous! I can't be blamed for the blasted snake. You should never have opened the door. The place is surrounded by dense vegetation. Anyway, it was most likely harmless.'

'But I wasn't in the mood to appreciate that!' Her green eyes suddenly glittered with tears. 'Go away, Jay. I *hate* you. I don't think I've ever hated anyone so much in my life!'

'Poor little girl!' He smiled grimly. 'Probably far better in most ways if you do. All right, you'd better call it a night at that. I'll take a look around the place again before I turn in. I won't disturb you. Your revolt has registered. You look played out. Goodnight, Miss Kent. I don't think there's a lock on the door, but a chair is often useful.'

'Jay?' She found her voice at last.

115

'Yes?' He turned back, as arrogant as Lucifer, his silvery gaze radiant.

'I was talking wildly. I didn't mean that!'

'You do. Go to bed—go on, beat it, or I'll tuck you in myself!'

'I'll be better in the morning,' she said quietly.

'I sure hope so. You're trembling all over the place at the moment. I'm sure you've got a couple of aspirin. Take them. I was a damned fool bringing you in the first place. I should have dumped you on another station.'

'You're a very cruel man!' she said, spacing her words. 'I just can't see my way through all your labyrinthine complexities.'

'You would if we stayed too long in the one place. Look, Melanie, I'm trying to be as kind as I know how. While you're here, *anywhere,* on my property, you're my business. That means I give the orders and you obey them.'

'Fine! Go ahead, *give* one!'

'No damn fear, I'm going to teach you a lesson!'

A storm of alarm swept through her. She was frightened, he looked so tall and adamant. She turned and raced away from him and the door slammed. It didn't have a lock, but she rammed the chair against it, a frail defence that could disintegrate in a moment. What a shocking man! She would never forgive him too soon.

Despite himself, Jay found himself laughing. He could hear her ram the chair up under the doorknob. He stared up at the ceiling and groaned: 'Miss Melanie Kent, you tempt me. You do, you silly, ungrateful little wretch!' There was silence on the other side of the wall. He laughed under his breath and walked out into the cooling, calming night air. This might make a lovely story for her grandchildren. Miss Melanie Kent was going to beg forgiveness in the morning or else!

CHAPTER SIX

Such hopes proved a wasted effort. Hours later, Jay became conscious that someone was moving outside the bungalow. He sat up quickly, his eyes glittering in the dark. He had learned to rely on himself in every situation and he had no fears of anybody or anything. Besides, he had a good understanding of what was afoot. Usually they would wait to make contact in the morning. He was totally alert now, and in a way it was a relief. The long hours had been mostly sleepless, though he had dozed off half fitfully from time to time. He was dressed except for Ron's too tight shirt and his leather boots.

He looked towards the bedroom door. Melanie had not stirred or made a sound—sleeping the deep sleep of the innocent, he supposed. He had a clear realisation of where the faint noises were coming from. There was a rifle beside him. He was ready for any kind of action, but he didn't think it would be necessary, even firing off a few rounds for effect. It would frighten Melanie out of her wits in any case. A detailed examination o' the bungalow's grounds showed recent signs of a disturbed bushland.

Jay moved deftly, with purpose, looking out the window for some glimpse of a moving figure. For a minute no movement showed, then a dark shadow began to race back from the bungalow into the bush. Jay moved the curtain to one side, then dropped it again. That short frantic dash told him everything he needed to know. He wouldn't see any of them until morning. No treachery of any kind was intended. Just as well! He would have trapped the lot of them.

'Jay?'

Melanie's soft voice claimed his attention. It was faltering and it made him turn and veer sharply back towards her. 'I'm here!'

He sounded immensely reassuring, wide awake and alert. 'What's wrong?' She moistened her lips with the tip of her tongue.

'Nothing, to my knowledge.'

'I thought I could hear someone moving about.'

'Good!' Only the sofa now was between them. 'I could use a cup of coffee.'

'What time is it?' she asked.

'I don't know.' He raised his wrist and checked the time from the luminous dial on his watch. 'It's almost four!'

'Do you really want a cup of coffee?'

'Would I say I did if I didn't?' He started towards the light switch. 'Have you slept at all?'

'I think I must have, but I don't want to go back to bed at all.'

'Good!' he said abruptly. The brilliant flare of light

could find no fault in her. She still wore slacks and the silk blouse, the fabric gleaming, her hair falling over her forehead and down the curve of her neck. She was the most sheltered little creature in the world, her hands crossed slightly in front of her breast, a woman's time-honoured position of defencelessness. Jay's multiple irritations seemed to quicken into a raw sensitivity. She was becoming more and more disturbing as the hours passed. His voice lifted imperatively, sharply. He knew he was snapping, but he couldn't help it.

'Are you properly awake?' he asked. 'You look dreamy!'

'Of course.' She sounded hurt. 'Is there anybody outside, Jay?'

'It makes no difference,' he said, hunting up Ron's shirt. 'They won't properly show themselves until daylight. Black coffee. Come on, on the double! No sugar.'

She turned about instantly, saying she would get it. She sounded like an obedient child, all the passionate mutiny of the night before gone. He avoided looking at her, his arrogant nostrils flaring, a hard set to his mouth and chin.

In the kitchen Melanie splashed her face with cold water and wiped it with a paper towel. The thought of the snake made her pick up her feet and look carefully into every corner. She had thought she would suffer nightmares on account of that snake, but she had slept dreamlessly until she had woken with a start, uncertain in that first instant of her bearings. It would be damnable for a while trying to get used to all these natural hazards. Jay, she suspected, was fed up with her. He cheeks burned with her recollections. How could sh have told him she hated him? It was so uncontrolled and so childish. Worse, it couldn't have been further from the truth. It must have been that single unaccustomed drink.

Jay walked into the kitchen without a sound. It was so disconcerting the way he moved like a sleek, beautifully co-ordinated animal. Melanie grabbed the jug and filled it, anxious now to placate him. He was leaning against the cupboard watching her, making no move to help. She walked quickly back and forth, not speaking to him either. Presently the jug boiled and she poured the hot water over the instant coffee.

'I want to talk to you,' she said at last, very small and slender.

'All right! *Talk.*'

'You sound so hard,' she complained.

'I *feel* it. All right, Melanie, don't look like that. Talk.'

'I'm sorry about last night, Jay. I apologise. It must have been the drink you gave me.'

'Is that important? You meant it!'

'I didn't, Jay,' she insisted.

'All right, who cares?'

'*I* do.'

'All right! We'll start all over again.' He caught her arm and found it trembling. Her white skin was flushed and her mouth looked distressed. 'So help me!' he said oddly. The harsh light from the naked bulb streamed down over them. Her green eyes were tormented. Somehow she had moved closer to him, not thinking with her mind but acting under some kind of comIsion.

'No, Jay!' she pleaded.

His hand tightened on her arm, drawing her closer still. 'There's got to be some antidote. Think of it like snakebite.'

'No.'

'You've got to pay for what you said to me,' he said hardly.

'I really shall, Jay, but not this way.'

'How beautiful you are!' he said with self-mockery. 'My first impulse is to strangle you.'

'Have your coffee, *please*.' She stared rigidly past his dark head.

'Give it to me,' he ordered.

'All right, if you'll let my arm go.'

She spun around with fervour, frightened of him, frightened of herself. His handsome dark face looked relentless, impatient of whatever she was hiding. Her behaviour *was* erratic, irrational—she knew that. She had come to Australia to be with David, and now there was Jay. He was considerably older and far more experienced than she was.

'Melanie——?' he began.

'Yes, what?'

'I haven't had a cup of coffee this early with a woman in my life!' The attractive amused lilt was back in his voice again.

'Now that you mention it I've never been alone with a man but my father at this hour of the morning!' she confessed.

'Surely not?'

There was a cutting edge now that was annihilati
She turned back to him, clearly exposed in the s

lighting. 'Don't speak to me like that, Jay,' she begged.

'You tell me *that*, yet Dave is madly in love with you!'

'What's so peculiar about that?' she asked.

'It's not Dave's way!' he said dryly, his eyes intent on her.

'Is it yours?'

'You didn't have to race away last night!' he said crisply.

'I don't have to race away now!' An emerald blaze was deep in her eyes.

'Don't delude yourself, little one! I find you very, very beautiful, unaccountably disturbing!'

'Why change your mind?' She spoke softly, oddly off-key.

'If I'd said that last night,' he said dryly, 'I'd have scared you half to death.'

'*Hardly!*' She was coming burningly alive again.

'No?' He swung her round to face him, watching the way her hair and her skin gleamed in the light.

'Jay MacCallister, don't make me hate you,' she said softly.

'I thought you already did!'

She could scarcely credit it, what there was between them. 'Don't put our relationship at risk. *Please*, Jay!'

'Now that's what I call common sense,' he drawled. 'What a pity it's four o'clock in the morning. Time enough for common sense when the sun comes up!'

She jerked her head back distractedly. 'I love David.'

'Of course you do. That's why you've been goading to kiss you for the past twenty-four hours. Let's get it over for the first and last time. After all, it's all in the family!'

'I'm going to fight you!' Her eyes blazed and her teeth bit into her bottom lip, bringing up frantic colour.

'I almost admire your impudence!' He laughed a little and pulled her into his arms, rendering her struggles futile. 'I'm not going to kiss you, Melanie. I was only testing you.'

'You beast!' she shouted. 'If I could get free, I'd kill you!'

'Irredeemable, Melanie. Would you sacrifice your immortal soul for me?'

'Let me go, Jay!' she said, in a broken voice.

'No.'

'For God's sake!' She tried to rouse herself. The danger was real. She was responding to him as she never thought it possible to respond to another human being.

'I will soon enough!' he said tautly. 'It's a strange thing, but I'm not going to now!'

He lowered his head and she gave up her breath. It was useless to fight him. She didn't want to. His touch was like heated gold. She turned up her own mouth, uninvited, feeling the same urgent desire, and her body miraculously moulded itself to his hard frame. She had no thought of resisting but only of meeting this ruthless demand. His hand was closed tightly about her nape, shaping it, holding her head steady under his questing mouth. Its mastery astonished her, brought her to wild life. She wanted this drowning, pulsing excitement to go on for ever. She was half lying against him, her balance gone, following his lead so exact she could have been accused of what he had said—a reckless, urgent seduction. Sparks were flying under his fingertips, moving across her cheek to explore its contours, the shell of her ear. A wide swathe of her hair almost came between them and he brushed it aside, murmuring something she was beyond hearing. She wanted to remember nothing before him ...

She wasn't a woman at all, but liquid fire. His arms were tightening, tightening, the pressure of his mouth deepening into a hungry passion. The fire leapt, wiping away the past, the present. It shrivelled her without a sound, arousing her to a kind of desperation when she wished for so much more ...

'Melanie!'

His voice sounded so harsh and clipped it shocked her cruelly. His hands shifted from her face to her shoulders, holding her back in flagrant protest. He had measured his folly. She still had her eyes closed, her soft mouth burning. She had betrayed herself on a grand scale. So many emotions consumed her it was impossible to regain control of herself. She was changed beyond belief, and Jay had forced the change on her whether he had intended it or not. A great wind should rise up and sweep her away from him. She would never escape this moment. It was her dream for the living.

He said her name again and shook her gently. Was there an edge of tenderness in his voice? Melanie could not be sure—she could only envy him his self-possession. What had happened wasn't even discussable. It had only to be censored.

'I can't talk to you if you keep your eyes shut!' he ~~d.~~

'Then I'll be glad!'

'Could be I haven't stopped kissing you!'

Her eyes flew open and he smiled at her. 'There! See, you can open them!'

'It was my way of blocking you out,' she explained.

'It will all end happily ever after, princess,' he assured her gently, 'don't worry!'

'I'm not worrying, Jay. I've been kissed before.'

'I expected that. You can't imagine what effect you had on me.'

His eyes were very steady as they moved over her face, her lips parted and throbbing, her hair spilling wildly about her flushed face. She looked intensely feminine, the flutter of her heart visible against her silk shirt. 'Sure you don't want me to apologise?' he asked dryly.

'You're not sorry!'

'Neither are you!'

'I *am*!' she said urgently, her eyes locked in his.

He jeered softly, 'Don't be such a little hypocrite! You were just acting naturally. I've still got my arms around you—haven't you noticed?'

'Yes, you excel at this kind of thing. I'm dazed. It's been a long series of bizarre events!'

'And just consider it's not the end of them. *If you stay!*'

'I think you've been waiting for me to make a wrong move!'

'What a thing to say!' Unexpectedly he put out a finger and drew it along her cheek. 'I think it's about time the sun came up, don't you? Night time entitle us to make fools of ourselves!'

'Not you, Jay! You're in every way remarkable!'

'You're pretty intoxicating yourself. Don't make too much of a kiss, Miss Kent.'

'Rather, let's forget it!' she said, arching away from him.

'But how can I when reality exceeds even the imagination?' When she least expected it, he let her go and she almost stumbled.

'I cannot and *will* not let you kiss me again,' she said sharply.

His smile reached the brilliant depths of his eyes. 'No need to get yourself uptight. When I want to, I will!'

'I suppose you would at that!' she said in a helpless, inadequate voice. 'So much for the strong coffee!'

'Boil the jug again, there's a good girl. We'll make a little housewife of you yet.' Jay stood up and moved away from her. Melanie could still feel the warmth of his body, the strength of his arms that seemed so easily to crush her. The touch of his mouth still lingered on her own. She drew a jagged little breath and looked out the window, surprised to see that the sky had lightened to a soft exquisite grey with long streaks of lemon and pink.

'It's morning!' she said almost plaintively.

'Thank God for that!'

They came out of the bush one by one, swerving in behind their leader—bush myalls, as much a part of their background as the billabongs and the bauhinia trees, the heat haze that danced around their glossy ck bodies. The glaring light was harsh on their

126

grimacing faces, drunk on a kind of constant, induced rage. They were excited and began to call out to Jay, who walked straight out to meet them, telling Melanie to remain inside in no uncertain terms. She watched him walk away, his dark face expressionless.

Nearing the myalls, he suddenly swung his arm in a powerful movement, a tremendous vitality and authority emanating from his tall, wide-shouldered body. The stamping and the antics that Melanie didn't find in the least bit funny suddenly stopped.

'You know who I am,' she heard him call clearly. 'MacCallister. What do you want?'

All of them save one scuffed the ground, the bunches of leaves tied around their bare ankles swishing the dust. The leader, a tribal elder, moved a few paces forward, his arms jerking, white circles drawn round his eyes. He was old but impressive, still capable of treachery and violence. He was panting, his breath rattling his bony frame, sweat running down his glistening, painted face, and into his beard, white like his sparse stiffened hair.

Melanie stood rooted to an inside window. She could feel herself shaking. She knocked back into a chair and it fell over. She straightened it, shaking her head, and when she looked back again, the whole party had Jay surrounded. They were almost naked, their bodies painted and feathered with down, the points of their spears shining grotesquely in the sunlight. The old man was cursing violently, almost dancing an unbridled corroboree. Jay, head and shoulders over him, his hair blue-black in the light, was apparently unperturbe￼

even though the old man kept jabbing the air with his spear.

Panic seared through Melanie in full measure. These were people of a primitive culture. They related only to themselves and their own laws. There were eight of them, and one of Jay. He was making no attempt to stop the old man's angry flow, and he looked violent, ruled by some kind of passion, an unpredictable old savage with hideous cicatrices over his chest and extending down on either side of his abdomen. His heavy spear looked barbarous and it was much too near Jay's head. She was aware that her breath was hissing and that the sunlight was blazing across the verandah in an untamed golden flow.

As if he had had enough, Jay's hand suddenly came down hard on the old fellow's shoulder, almost pressing him into the ground. He looked tough and confident and he had quite a hold on the old myall. Melanie couldn't hear his voice, she could only remember the hard passion of his mouth and how vital he was to her safety. These people wished to settle their own quarrel. This was their land. Theirs was a prehistoric culture. How did one deal with them? Jay had deliberately set out to do just that. What had Spider done? She tried to consider the possibilities. Something serious to match the old man's anger. Surely he hadn't killed someone? Taken a woman? It happened in all societies, not only the primitive.

The blacks in the circle were quiet now. Melanie could detect no attitude of hostility towards Jay. He laced his hand on each one of their heads, then ruptly they broke ranks, withdrawing one by one into the bush with no sense of hurry almost as if they had all the time in the world to wait for Spider to come back to be punished. Jay looked after them thoughtfully, then he turned about and started towards the bungalow. Melanie felt she had waited for him all her life, her relief was so intense she almost flew out on to the verandah.

'For heaven's sake, tell me what's happening!' she demanded.

'They want to kill Spider,' Jay told her.

'Good grief!' She very nearly slammed into him with shock.

He dropped his arm round her shoulder and marched her back into the house. 'Didn't I tell you to keep out of sight? As for Spider, he's been warned over and over and the warnings haven't proved successful. It's the old fellow's wife. Spider can't and won't keep away from her.'

'How mind-boggling! How old is she?'

'About fifteen.'

'But that old fellow's ancient,' she gasped, 'and so ugly!'

'Yes, but he's still pretty romantic. The girl belongs to him. He's Opal, the head man, an elder and a very important person. Spider should know better. The old fellow could if he liked hand her on to Spider, but he's not going to do that. He's very sensitive about his diminishing powers. He was a great warrior once with a considerable number of women. Spider going off with his wife has resulted in a loss of authority and prestige. He's a surly old devil and dangerous. I wouldn't lik Spider's chances if he ever caught up to him!' Delibe ately he pushed her into a chair, his manner offhand. 'Sit down, Melanie, your cat's eyes are blazing but your face is very white.'

'I believe you. There hasn't been a dull moment since I arrived. What are you going to do now?'

'I'm going to get Spider out of here, far away from this devil-woman. An evil spirit has got into poor old Spider. He's always chasing women, as it happens, but he can't chase this one, however much she is to his taste. Old Opal is to be feared. To begin with, he's one of the old sorcerers. If he doesn't actually kill Spider himself, he just might avenge himself supernaturally. Knowing Spider the way I do, I think he'd rather face a spear.'

Melanie flashed him a quick look, her throat dry. 'What about the girl?' she asked. 'What does she say?'

Jay leant back against the table and closed his eyes. 'My dear Melanie, women have no say at all. Probably she knows nothing about it and cares less.'

'Then what did you tell them?'

'I told them if they attempted to take the law into their own hands, I'd hand them all over to the white man's court. I'd even fly them there myself, all locked up in chains. The best thing I can do is get Spider out of here. He's become uncontrollable about this girl.'

'But won't they wait for him?'

'They're out there, certainly, but they won't touch him while I'm here. I've plenty big fella magic myself and I've got wings. Anyway, they've given their word.'

'They could be lying,' she argued.

'No. You can only guess at my powers of persuasion, le English girl.'

'Well, I'm glad you're not as frightened as I am!' she said shakily.

'Don't tempt me to comfort you.' His voice was silky, racing like fire along her veins. 'I know better now,' she assured him. '*That* was just an emotional storm. It's gone away.'

'Oh? Which way did it go?'

'Don't fool with me, Jay,' she begged.

'I can't help it, especially when you're only a foot away. Now, I was going to suggest a hearty breakfast.'

'Do you never stop eating?' she accused him unfairly.

'Only at the usual times. Besides, it gives you something to do. Women have to be kept busy in a kitchen, otherwise they get unhappy. There's nothing much else I can direct you to, short of swooping on you. Ron should come in directly. He would have broken camp at first light. Heaven knows I can't wait to get my hands on Spider. I'll give him Don Juan! I might even have to wallop him a few times to satisfy old Opal.'

'You mean *hit* him?'

'It's a kindness. You don't have to watch. Better than a spear in the back at any rate. With any luck he'll bawl his head off and old Opal will be satisfied, the blood-thirsty old devil. I'll make it look convincing. Spider's about your size.'

'You're serious?' she asked.

'Of course I am. Bush justice.' He added suddenly, 'You've got shadows under your eyes—not that they don't suit you. It's a very fragile effect. You'd better grab a little rest while Spider and I fight it out.'

'If he's got any sense he won't show up at all.'

'He's here *now*!'

131

Melanie sat straight up, her back stiffening. 'Really?'

Jay nodded his dark head. 'I didn't like to point it out to Opal, but he's slipping. He's not the tracker he used to be and Spider's one of my best. He must have led Ron quite a dance before doubling back to the bungalow. Probably he saw the plane. I'll give him another minute or two before he comes crawling through the back door.'

'Are you sure you haven't psychic powers yourself?' Melanie tilted her blonde head back. 'I think I'm having a bad time of it.'

'You won't regret any of it, Melanie!' he said, the laugh back in his voice. 'Think of the stories you can tell your grandchildren. How you came all the way out to Australia to love and adventure!'

'My first skirmish with a tiger!' Melanie laughed ruefully.

'Now what does that mean?' he asked.

'A sort of comparison.'

Jay's face was amused, vividly handsome, wondrously self-contained. 'I had no idea! As a matter of fact I think I deserve a lot of credit for restraint.'

'We can't agree about that,' she said.

'Then my restraint was a wicked waste!' He started to move and Melanie moved at the same time. 'Not *you*, camellia face,' he called to her and she stared after him as if mesmerized. In one long graceful lunge he was at the back door, flinging it open, his voice ʳeely. 'Come in, Spider. How glad I am to see you!'

A young aboriginal boy, his black eyes a wonderful in his face, hurtled through the opening and mea-

sured his slender length on the kitchen floor. 'Mornin',
Boss, just you?'

'Too bad, Spider,' Jay said kindly. 'The whole camp
is out there on the other side.'

'Been waitin' to see you, Boss.'

'Well, you'd better get up or you'll never get another
chance!' Jay rounded abruptly on Melanie, who had
come to the other door. 'Go into the other room,' he
said, frowning, very much MacCallister.

'Mornin', miss!' said Spider respectfully, hauling
himself to his feet, his black eyes still huge with fright,
his skin coffee-coloured with his mixed blood. He was
drenched in sweat and covered with small bleeding
scratches. Melanie felt her heart go out to him in compassion. He was obviously waiting for her to put in a
good word for him.

'You're going to punish him, Jay?' she asked on
Spider's behalf, half fearful of Jay's brilliant gaze, the
hard set of his jaw.

'*Wrong!*' Jay bit out emphatically. 'I'm going to talk
to him. Would you please leave us? You might hear a
few things you've never heard before.'

She withdrew in a hurry and Jay slammed the door
on her to give Spider his fullest attention. Melanie re-
treated to the sofa and gave a great sigh. She felt worn
out. This was unbelievable. She couldn't even begin
to contemplate what else might be in store for her—
flood, fire, drought, wild electrical storms, choking dust.
Jay's voice was a dark rolling thunder, Spider's a shrill
shout. She put her hands over her ears, but she could
still hear Spider protesting violently, denying all th
warnings he had supposedly been given by Opal. I

133

thundered again: 'Liar!' and Spider desisted abruptly, realising the uselessness of his protests, accepting whatever the Boss considered best for him.

Melanie tipped her head back. It was aching. She was crying out for hours and hours of interrupted sleep. Let Jay cope with all this. He was a strong man, ruthless when he had to be. This was his property, these were his people. He was sure to get them all out of their predicament. At least poor wretched Spider was safe. Opal would have claimed him, surely, if the dust storm hadn't diverted them to this place. She had never experienced such a turbulent time in her life. Life with Sybil was tame compared to this. She would be a wreck by the time she arrived at Coorrabin, but didn't it look as if there too she would find herself in a difficult situation?

CHAPTER SEVEN

So Melanie came to Coorrabin, but whatever her reasons when she left London, she was no longer in love with David. It seemed now that she hadn't even known herself in those days, and she couldn't resurrect her feelings now that she had lost them. In her lonely search for love she realised now that what she had felt for David was a dream of love without knowing what love was about. He own sensuality had been revealed to her, and it had not been David she had responded to so desperately. She was fortunate perhaps that she had found this out. Self-knowledge was important and it

134

could guide her in her future life. She wasn't fickle and her letters to David hadn't been frauds. She had simply found out that a warm and comfortable relationship, though enviable, could yet be second best. Facts were facts. She couldn't believe what she had once, but her response to Jay had been so enormous that her constant recollections exaggerated her sense of loss and pain out of all proportion. If she hadn't known anything about falling in love before, she did now, and she was afraid of it.

Yet David looked at her in the old way, with pride and possession. She couldn't begin to explain herself; she would just have to accept that she, like thousands before her, had suffered a change of heart. With David's arms around her, his mouth claiming hers in front of a whole welcoming party, she could scarcely have drawn back, not with Jay's mocking silvery gaze on her bringing up the wild colour they all attributed to David. When the colour died down they realised how very fragile she looked, still suffering the effects of continuous travelling, so that first week was allowed to slip away in a glorious golden haze just resting and settling into her new environment.

In a way her change of heart was tragic, for Coorrabin was perfect—a secret mansion that some perverse wizard had set down in the wilds. Melanie had expected the homestead to be beautiful, an emphatic statement of the MacCallister wealth and position, but she hadn't been prepared for its extraordinary drawing power, the dazzling incongruity of a magnificent colonial mansion in the middle of nowhere. A milli¬ trackless acres and great flood plains bordered by ancient rose-red dunes and peaks of the Simpson Desert, a place of death and evil spirits to the aborigines and looked upon with great fear. It was barbaric, yet it was splendid, and at first sight it had taken her breath away. It explained Jay and to a degree David. A great heritage would put a man apart—all that extraordinary backdrop of space, limitless free space. She was used to historic London and its splendid past, but this ancient unsettled land had an overwhelming fascination. It had an unique, primeval quality too deeply felt for any words properly to describe it, and Melanie knew it would take her years even to try. It was exciting and it was frightening. In a way, it was like Jay.

With four successive good seasons, Coorrabin stock was grazing far out into the desert, for it had flamed into life, its rippling, blazing sands covered with the flowering annuals and transients, the eternal spinifex, the saltbush and cotton bush, the apple and emu bush, the pink parakeelya the cattle could live on for months without need of water, the never-ending vistas of green waving pussy tails, the lilac lambs' tails, the vast carpets of paper daisies, the lilies and hibiscus, Sturt's blood-red desert pea.

The Simpson, Melanie had discovered, was a remarkable place, not a real desert at all though it was dreadful beyond words in time of drought. But now, after rain, miraculous miles of wild flowers stretched away to the horizon, blindingly beautiful under the imperious sun. It seemed to her when she first looked at these desert gardens that she had never seen a more spectacular sight in her life. It was so unexpected and really bizarre for a wild heart to bloom like a pagan

136

oasis. This was Coorrabin, almost a forbidden kingdom, for she had entered it under false pretences, and its ruler was Jay.

Yet David had accompanied her that day. An increasingly possessive and difficult to handle David. He seemed to alternate between moods of considerable charm and a hard aggression almost amounting to menace. The purpose of her long journey was to marry him, and she had better watch out if she changed her mind. It had only taken her the week to discover that David could be fanatical about some things and less time to find that Hilary Lyall-Watson considered her a usurper who had seized David's love wrongly and shamefully, using her blonde fragility for her own advantage, a passport into an exclusive world of position and power —for, womanlike, Hilary had divined at once Melanie's true feelings about David.

For her part, Melanie had been somewhat shocked to find Hilary very much at ease at the homestead the same day that she herself arrived. Hilary, as a close family friend and neighbour, concerned about David's injury, had flown over to help out in any way she could and stay on to meet the English visitor. So sure of herself was she, so thick her beautifully tanned skin, she was still there by the end of the next day, though David, at times, was alarmingly rude to her. Yet Hilary was attractive, an almond-eyed brunette with a decided look of purpose to her, and her father was a very rich man.

At their first silent moment when introductions were being made, and Melanie, confused by the ardour David's greeting, met those challenging dark eyes the first time, she recognised at once that Hilary saw her as the enemy to be defeated by fair means or foul. No English miss could possibly stand up to the rigours of outback life. Though her manner had been friendly if slightly patronising she obviously considered herself the better woman on her home ground, which very likely she was. She looked super-efficient, outgoing and direct. It was Melanie who was the mermaid out of water and her tricks wouldn't work in the brilliant sunlight. Moreover, Hilary and Susan were close friends and conspirators and Susan and Derryn were flying in at the week-end for a family dinner-reunion-welcome-to-Melanie, by which time Hilary would have sent in a detailed report on the latest visitor to Coorrabin.

All that first week Melanie saw little of Jay. He started out very early in the morning and returned about sundown. There was a marked constraint between Jay and David, almost an incompatibility, but Greg's approach to his eldest brother was a mixture of hero-worship and an easy-going brotherly affection which was really a deep, abiding love. Greg, Melanie quickly found out, was totally engaging, the easiest of the brothers to get on with. David was not nearly so pleasant here in his own home as he had been in London and Jay was too busy anyway to be entertaining a house guest.

The only time Melanie had to study him was from under her lashes at dinner. It was almost the only way, for David watched both of them like a hawk, so absurdly jealous and ready to magnify the briefest exchange of glances that Melanie was beginning to find attitude intolerable. David with his possessive nature could very easily stifle a woman. In fact, Melanie grew increasingly to realise that he would react better to a relationship where the woman cared that bit more than he did. She realised too that Jay did have an over-shadowing effect on his brothers, but it was quite natural and unintentional, for Jay on his home ground had an uncompromising air of authority. He was immensely dynamic, so it was inevitable that David with his tendency towards egocentricity should resent being second in line to the human dynamo that was his brother Jay—a man, moreover, who was hardly aware of his own matchless force and the allegiance it inspired. Jay was MacCallister by temperament as much as being the eldest son. He was passionately devoted to this vast station, returning its rewards with equal hard work. His was the almost excessive vitality and dedication, the fighting spirit that had made heroes of the pioneers. David was the Brutus to Jay's Caesar, with the urge for power but half frightened of it and unequipped to handle it.

With his right arm in plaster it was obvious from his different moods that he felt more than ever reduced, and his gaze was none too gentle when it rested on Melanie. He watched her constantly, as though she could at an instant transfer her affections to Jay. That she had done so already was the extraordinary, indefensible thing, and it worried her. David when he felt threatened was like a time bomb ready to go off.

The afternoon Greg had begged off his jobs to show Melanie around the property on the back of his motor bike had been like a breath of fresh air after David stifling attentions. Greg was so blissfully uncomplica

139

and his friendly, unfeigned admiration could be kept well within bounds. The only man, she discovered, who could make her heart beat at a fantastic rate was Jay, and Jay was plainly keeping well out of the way. The land was Jay's great passion as David told her over and over as if she wished to dispute it. Yet it was a strange feeling wanting to be near Jay and not being able to at all.

The next best thing was Coorrabin, the formal beauty of the magnificent old homestead and its starkly brilliant setting like a pearl in a steel claw. The following week when she had realised her bearings a little she would ask to take out one of the horses. Though the station was mechanised to a tremendous degree it still kept up a fine stable for the love of horses, and the pleasure in riding them could never be supplanted.

There was nothing whatever for Melanie to do in the way of housework except perhaps arranging the flowers if she wished, for Coorrabin boasted an excellent housekeeper and a staff of dusky housegirls whose greatest wish had been to work up at the Big House. Mrs Rigby, the housekeeper, trained them, and from what Melanie could see she trained them well even if she couldn't curb their melting giggles, and they had fits of them, being fascinated apparently by Melanie's very fair hair and white skin when they had never moved off Coorrabin all their lives and even white women had their skin deeply kissed by the sun.

The Saturday evening that Susan and Derryn arived, Melanie dressed carefully for dinner. Susan had en perfectly pleasant, but with reservations, as igh she sympathised with Melanie's wish to marry her brother, but would much rather have David settle for Hilary, who was in every possible way suitable and already an old friend. Hilary was the right sort of person for David. She would make him an excellent wife. Being well bred, Susan didn't point out any of these things, but Melanie was left in no doubt of Susan's true feelings. She was extremely good-looking, very polished and poised, to Melanie's surprise more like Jay than any of them, though she shared David's and Greg's blue eyes. Jay was the only one to have inherited his father's striking light eyes and unquenchable energy. The blue eyes in the family came from their dead mother, whose portrait hung alongside other family portraits in the long gallery of the first floor.

The portrait Melanie liked best of all was the one of Jay's father that hung in the study. She liked the look of Jason MacCallister II. He looked a good man, a man of great generosity of spirit, a dominating man certainly, an unattainable sort of man, but not the ghastly tyrant, the demon who had tormented David's childhood and adolescence with his indifference. Susan in the brief moment she had mentioned her father had worn such a desolate look, as though she could never console herself to his lasting absence. One simply didn't love a tyrant like that. David had given her a cold and distant view of his father when Melanie had seldom seen a more striking and stable face, the face of a protector and provider, not the grim cause of a father-complex. David, she thought, would be far better away from Coorrabin on a property of his own where he could be master of his own universe. This was obviou, important to him, a key to his character.

141

Not a day had passed that he hadn't brought up the topic of their early marriage. A restlessness was in Melanie now to make her position clear. After that, having burnt all her boats, she would have to find a job and pay back the money David had sent her for her fare. She was very good at her line of work and now that she was here in Australia, she should take the opportunity of seeing as much of the country as she could. This she thought in her philosophical moments, but mostly, and at night, the thought of Jay's going out of her life subjected her to a controlled but excessive tension. Whatever unhappiness lay in store for her, she had widend her boundaries of knowledge. Finally she would have to leave Coorrabin. Such things happened. Human beings were unpredictable, inconstant.

It seemed to her too that ever since her mother died, life had been a kind of struggle or there had been little real happiness in it for her. Perhaps she was too sensitive. David had seemed to offer her a new life in a land of great vitality. Now she felt as distant to him as the moon, and her feelings were mixed with pity for him and anger at herself. She felt shamed by her own defection, forgetting that it was the easiest thing in the world to make a mistake. So many mistakes were made every day and all in the name of love, but very few had the privilege of knowing even a few moments of ecstasy. However much Jay had hurt her by just being Jay, she would never regret having met him.

honour of the occasion Jay decided to use the big nal dining room for the first time, opening back olding cedar doors so that they could look into the main drawing room with its splendid matching chandelier, and its superb antique furniture that went happily with the deep sofas and armchairs he had had custombuilt: 'So necessary if one gives a thought to comfort!' as he mentioned in passing. Both rooms had carved marble fireplaces surmounted by large oval gilt mirrors, balanced by paintings and various treasures in bronze and porcelain, with beautifully detailed plaster ceilings in the same design and centred by a rose from which the chandeliers were appended.

They were certainly the grandest rooms Melanie had ever been in in her life, but they contributed in no way to her feeling of isolation. She had seemed to be moving in a strange void ever since she had come down to dinner. Jay had only spoken directly to her once, his fingers touching hers briefly as he passed her a predinner drink: 'Some concoction Derryn dreamed up!' he explained carelessly, but the touch of his skin against hers made all the old magnetism start working. The sheen of his eyes in his dark face was extraordinary, lancing over her in an instant, missing absolutely nothing before he turned away to offer his sister the dry sherry she wanted.

For one minute only did Melanie allow herself the luxury of looking at him, then David came in to claim her, smooth and handsome, asking her to adjust the black sling that Edna, the housekeeper, had rigged up for him. His blue eyes had been blazing, proud of her beauty, his head lowering to drop a real kiss somewhere between the lobe of her ear and the curve of her chin. He seemed in good spirits, more like the old David, b Melanie had the feeling it wouldn't, couldn't last. A

143

dinner, David would want to discuss marriage plans again, reminding her of the coals she had heaped on her head.

Over the gleaming table with its beautiful place settings Hilary studied the youthful, excessively slender figure of the English girl. Mermaid wasn't a bad name for her. That was Jay's opinion and he had let it fall. But who needed a mermaid in the Big Country if she could survive at all? Mercifully there had been no date set for a wedding nor even an engagement, and the longer they held off, the more hopeful Hilary became. She was willing to believe the family weren't completely satisfied with Dave's choice either. Susan was being very gracious, unbending by the minute, but then Susan had the highest regard for good manners. Greg, of course, was smitten, but that was to be expected at his age. Jay, who was quite a lady-killer and a brilliant, uncatchable catch, was almost distant, his strange eyes, the most alive eyes Hilary had even seen in a face, resting on Melanie only in passing. No doubt he had come to the conclusion that Dave had made a mistake, and Jay would be a powerful ally.

For five years now Hilary had come to regard Dave as her property. In many ways he was an obsessive young man, difficult and contradictory, but as soon as they were married she would change all that. She had the balance Dave lacked and she was strong. There was no need for Dave to stay with the MacCallister chain if he didn't want to. In a few years' time he would come into a considerable amount of money and they could what they liked, though she would always want to at least her winters in the Inland. Dave needed *her*, not this silver-haired wraith in his care.

Melanie Kent quite frankly was an appalling mistake. She should never have come here, and she wasn't too far from that realisation herself, for there was a trapped look in the depths of her eyes like a small wild creature backed into a corner. Hilary knew the look. The girl had little in common with Jay either, for she scarcely turned her head his way, preferring to bestow her little half-smiles on Greg and Derryn, who in a very short time seemed very taken with her. But then Derryn with his background was the complete Anglophil.

Hilary raised her silver goblet to her lips and sipped thoughtfully at the contents. She was accustomed to being hurt by Dave, but she would get him in the end even if she had to rope tie him. His passion for this little slip of a thing would pass if given enough time. She was pretty, very pretty indeed, with Dave and Greg and even Derryn in thrall, but she was ill at ease even if the men found her enticing like a lorelei on a rock. Men really did prefer blondes, but mercifully they seemed to settle for the more suitable brunettes with their lasting qualities.

Hilary tried to catch Dave's eye to force him to look at her. She had taken great pains with her dressing and make-up and she knew she looked her best, but Dave was leaning forward in his chair just devouring this Melanie. What had she done to him? Hilary could cheerfully have hurled her goblet at the green-eyed little witch in her delicious little dress showing all that delectable white skin. When she spoke, and she had to force herself to, there was no warmth in her voice.

145

'Do you ride, Melanie?' She caught Dave's eye then. He shot her a hard look.

'What the hell else do you expect?'

'I'm no expert, but yes!' Melanie said gently.

'Self-taught?' Hilary persisted, ignoring the consequences.

'No, I went to a riding school when I was about nine. My grandfather had a farm in Shropshire, and I used to spend nearly all my school holidays there. Grandfather loved horses and he knew a lot about them. I did most of my riding there.'

'In that beautiful green countryside!' Derryn enthused, looking at Melanie kindly.

'Why don't we all go out tomorrow?' Hilary suggested, running a disparaging eye over Melanie's slight physique. She didn't look as if she could hold a broom, let alone Jay's spirited horses.

'I'd have expected you to come up with such a brilliant idea!' Dave jeered, without putting up a pointless show of civility.

'Oh, gosh, Dave, I quite forgot about your arm!' Hilary said truthfully, the colour sweeping up under her golden skin.

'I could manage with one!' he said curtly.

'There's no hurry!' Jay interrupted, gazing at his brother reflectively.

'Don't let me stop you!' said Dave.

'Actually it was Melanie I was thinking about.'

'Well, I'd like to go!' Melanie said, looking directly at Jay for the first time.

'There! All I've got to do is stay in the saddle!' Dave burst out.

'You know better!' Jay said with crisp decision.

'Why don't *you* take Melanie out?' Greg challenged Jay artlessly. 'You haven't done a thing to entertain her since she arrived.'

'That's not Jay's job!' Dave began heatedly.

'Why not?' Susan looked at her brother sharply. 'Jay is head of the household, the host. Why are you getting so excited? He's not going to run off with her.'

'You can't keep out of anything, can you, Sue?' Dave said rudely.

'Now see here, Dave ...' Derryn started out.

'All right then, that's settled!' Jay announced, coming to a decision quite independent of any of them. Indeed he seemed detached. He turned his dark head towards Melanie, a smile at the corners of his mouth. 'Sunday I can spare. Which would you prefer, morning or afternoon?'

'Make it the morning!' Susan suggested. 'The only time I get to sleep in is the week-end. We can swim in the afternoon and have a barbecue tomorrow night.'

'That leaves me out!' Dave continued to glare at her.

'Don't blame us if you broke your arm!' Derryn said reasonably. 'You're a big boy now, you'll get on fine. We'll look after you.'

Dave shrugged and moodily picked up his spoon as if he was going to hurl it. 'You're not really thinking of going, are you, Melanie?'

'I'd like to, David.' Her green eyes in her cameo face weren't as serene as her voice.

'Oh, don't be such an old miser with this gorgeous

147

girl!' Greg complained. 'Assert yourself, Melanie. Say you're going.'

'*I'm going!*' She borrowed Greg's emphatic tone and smiled at him.

'Atta girl!' Greg looked back at his brother and made a double take. 'Hey, don't look at Melanie like that, you'll frighten her.'

'It seems as though she's going all the same!' Jay said in a dark, sardonic voice. 'You know, Melanie, you haven't shown us any of your sketchbooks, and young Oola with her quick eyes tells me you've covered page after page and they're very good.'

'Really?' Hilary said with unbelief.

'My only talent!' Melanie pointed out.

'By heaven, that's a lie!' Greg burst out sagely.

'If it wouldn't bore you, you're welcome to look at them,' Melanie smiled.

'We'd like to!' Susan supplied, leaning forward and looking interested. The golden light from the chandelier was spilling over Melanie's head. She looked extraordinarily beautiful to Susan's eyes, with her fine bones and her silvery colouring. Her eyes were intensely green, sea green, enhanced by thick dark eyelashes. She looked very cool and mysterious, very different from Hilary, who was suffering, Susan knew. Susan was very fond of Hilary. They shared a warm friendship, but Hilary didn't have a chance against this lovely, cool creature—not at night anyway. Hilary, in her honey-coloured jersey, looked vital and healthy, in every sense a sparkling outdoor girl, but she didn't have the sensuous appeal of this girl, however much Susan regretted it.

She was sorry and shocked by the force of Dave's jealous passion. He was such an ass sometimes. He had a thing about Jay, always on the defensive about nothing. Jay, although perfectly courteous, didn't seem at all intent on Dave's latest love, rather Greg had almost pressed him into taking Melanie out the next day. Anyway, Jay could handle it and Dave was Dave, never easy to get on with, but she loved him.

Thinking this, Susan sent her gaze winging to him, then proceeded to invite him and Melanie to come stay with them for a few days at Whirlwinds. Dave brightened in an instant, giving his charming smile, almost comically grateful to have Melanie to himself without Jay and Greg around. Susan, knowing him so well, started to smile herself. When Dave was good, he was very, very good, but the rest of the time he was a real cross. Her good sense told her he wouldn't suit Melanie at all. Melanie had such a sensitive look about her, and Dave could be a real savage. Melanie needed a strongly protective sort of man, a man to lean on, not the other way round. Dave would use a wife as a whipping post when the mood took him. He needed a woman who could give back as good as she got—someone like Hilary who was quite strong and could gallop him into the ground.

Attractions were stunning sometimes, she mused. Dave might have been very charming and romantic in London, but he was never at his best with Jay around, and they all had to admit it. He seemed to lose his individuality even if he had come right out of the juvenile delinquent stage. No one could say exactly what it was. Dave was good-looking and very capable

149

when he felt like it, well off in his own right, or he would be in a year or so. It was a question of degree, perhaps. Jay left the lasting impressions, the ones everyone who met him took away. He weakened Dave's impact. It was unintentional and unalterable—the worst of families when one member so easily outshone the others. Not that she minded, neither did Greg. It was Dave, the middle man, who couldn't accept what was common knowledge. Jay was MacCallister.

It was something of a relief when Oola and Mary came in to remove the dishes, their neat slender hands unobtrusively efficient, their shy smiles entrancing. Susan then suggested that they have coffee and perhaps a liqueur in the drawing room where they could look at Melanie's sketchbooks. With no drawing ability whatsoever Susan nevertheless had a great admiration for anyone artistically gifted and she was a great collector of modern Australian art. She began to talk about her collection as she got up, Derryn sliding back her chair and taking her arm. Jay was doing the same for Melanie, forestalling either of his brothers, while Dave professed himself irritated by his plaster cast. He excused himself for a few moments to see if Edna, an excellent nurse, could ease it for him, and perhaps scold him for lowering the sling. Hilary then insisted that she could do it every bit as well herself and ran after him. To her surprise, Melanie saw him stop, and despite all his show of hostility give in. Perhaps Hilary really did know how to handle him? She didn't feel up to it herself, which was no great help in a future wife.

Derryn and Susan went on ahead into the drawing room and after a minute Greg followed them. Jay turned to look at Melanie, his face faintly mocking but softened by the ghost of smile. 'What are you thinking about, Melanie? You have the softest faraway expression in your eyes.'

'Where I left my sketchbooks!' she said, as if it were the truth.

'And what before that?'

She was looking directly into his eyes, seemingly without an answer.

'Oh, never mind!' he said dryly. 'I can help you with the sketchbooks at least. Come this way, pretty bird!' His hand slid around her bare arm and Melanie felt her skin burning under his touch, as thin as gossamer. It was strange indeed to know her emotions could be as turbulent, as tearing as the wild sea when she had always thought herself a cool, controlled person. Her feelings were so real to her she imagined them palpitating in the air like butterflies, visible to them both.

His eyes sought hers, sure of her returned gaze. 'Don't spend your time asking yourself questions, Melanie. It's too wearing!'

'And painful!' she said briefly.

Everything about him, his tall lean body, his voice, the inclination of his dark head, the very sure touch of his hand, presented an enormous challenge to her, defying her to be herself, not the untouchable creature she was now pretending, shutting out Coraki, that brief, alien episode as if it had never happened. His hand had slipped to her wrist, inducing a taunting intimacy when she was struggling not to be drawn. She bent her head, her hair a silver-gilt aureole in the soft overhead lighting.

151

'What mood are you in now, Jay?' she asked almost fatalistically.

'I haven't seen you in a week,' was all he said.

'You've seen me at dinner.'

'That's not what I mean, Melanie. I'm going to peel all your inhibitions away from you, layer after layer. It would be worth it to get to the real you, not the little snow maiden.'

'I have a question,' she said shakily. 'Why do you want to?'

'I've said enough for now, Melanie.'

She drew a deep breath and tilted her head up again. 'You're an old hand at this kind of thing, Jay.'

'I'll be damned if I am!' he said softly, his hand for the moment hurting her, holding her still. 'It's the women who hound me!'

'*I* don't want to marry you!' she burst out, with a delicate flare to her nostrils.

He smiled at her, his diamond eyes gleaming. 'Even you could be beaten down in time,' he assured her.

'There you go again!' she said wryly.

They were moving towards the study, pausing near the open door, when Shaeki and Shilo, the one a beautiful shaded sable and the other a magnificent tri-colour, suddenly woke up and sprang up from the Persian rug and bounded at Jay and his visitor. Melanie, in arrears with the reflexes, came near to being knocked over by Shilo's seventy pounds and the force of his affection.

'Oh, Shilo!' He was attempting to lick her face, which she didn't mind in the least, but she was losing her balance. Jay's arm crossed over her, tightening and pulling her to one side while he ordered the dogs down

152

again. They subsided at once on to their favourite rug, still looking up expectantly. Their long sensitive faces looked so appealing, Melanie dropped to her knees, exclaiming over their beauty. She had already formed a bond of friendship with them and she loved the collie breed. They brought back so many happy memories of her childhood on her grandfather's farm.

'Oh, you're so beautiful!' she smiled, 'with your pedigrees a mile long. You remind me of home!'

The collies responded to all this admiration appreciatively; they were extremely attached to the family and willing to make a new friend. Jay looked down at Melanie's slender bent figure and the fantastically appealing picture all three presented, then he reached over abruptly and lifted her to her feet, leaving her blinking, surprised by his suddenness. His hands at her waist were strong and hard, his dark face lit by the brilliancy of his eyes. 'You're many things, aren't you, Miss Melanie Kent?' He seemed in no hurry to unlink his hands and she couldn't move. 'There are homes lined up for three of the pups. Sue's taking one back with her and Lys, another one of our friends, wants the other two. We'll keep two ourselves and one of them is yours. Take your pick.'

Her face reflected her pleasure and a curious disappointment. 'You seem to think I'm staying, Jay.'

'*Aren't* you?' He seemed poised on a knife edge, not hurting her but exerting enough pressure to keep her quite still.

'You know I can't accept yet. It would be lovely, though. I've already picked out my favourite—a female a shaded sable. Susan wants the blue merle. She's a ready named it Sapphire. Oh, Jay, let me go! You could send me mad!'

'I suppose you find it difficult to believe, but the feeling's mutual!'

'Greetings, you two!' Greg boomed behind them.

The collies, pleasurably excited again, leapt in unison, but Greg, used to their giant bounds, caught them neatly and balanced one on each arm, his fingers stroking their snowy collars.

'Good, Greg! You're just in time. Take the dogs out and settle them for the night!'

'Sure, Boss!' Greg agreed cheerfully. 'Come with me, Melanie. You can see the pups again. She's a sucker for them, did you know?'

'She's soft on a lot of things! By the way, here are your sketchbooks.' Jay moved around to the other side of the desk.

'But where did I leave them?' Melanie looked at him in surprise.

'I didn't ask. Oola brought them to me—she knew they belonged to you. You're a talented creature, aren't you?'

'Perfect is the only answer!' said Greg, scratching the dogs' ears. 'Coming, Melly?'

'No, she's *not*!' snapped Jay. 'That's only a wisp of a dress and Shilo has already attempted to knock her down.'

'Oh, I don't care!' said Melanie.

'Well, it makes a difference to me. Off you go, Greg!' Jay ordered briskly.

Greg chuckled and whistled up the dogs, who had e full run of a most beautiful home but treated it with ity. Melanie glanced after them rather wistfully.

'I know, I know, you wanted to go with Greg.'

She turned her gaze back to him, drowning. 'No, I didn't!' The admission was out. She couldn't control it. She might ache afterwards, but any snatched moment alone with Jay was precious.

'I'd have been quite depressed if you'd said yes.'

She hesitated, trying to see behind that vibrantly male face. 'Really, Jay?'

The pause seemed to lengthen, making the blood surge through her veins. 'Isn't it fairly evident?' he asked.

'I can't read your eyes at all!'

'Just as well! You wouldn't be standing there like a trusting child.'

'I don't understand you,' she said.

'Dead right!' His eyes narrowed over her. 'Try and let that little brain of yours function.'

'It's quite a good brain, actually,' Melanie defended.

'In some things. You're not a very good student of men!'

'Frankly I don't want to be,' she said. 'Just *one*!'

'And who might that be?'

'Would I tell you?'

'That depends. How long are you going to stay with us, Melanie?' He smiled at her, like a curl of flame, and she smiled back, her green eyes glowing, an odd stillness about both of them.

'And to think I never invited you!'

'Well, it's kind of you to let me stay on.'

'Perhaps I won't let you go away,' he mused.

'You might have an extremely difficult time stopping me, Jay.'

'We'll see!'

155

He was leaning back against the wide desk, the big portrait of his father, the one she liked so much, directly behind his head.

'I hope you weren't pressured into taking me out tomorrow?' she asked.

'Driven, no less!' he said abruptly. 'Unless I'm mistaken that's Dave coming to fetch us. Come along, Melanie, we can't fail him.'

CHAPTER EIGHT

MELANIE had just finished dressing when the sharp rap came on her door. She went to it hurriedly straightening the sun yellow collar of her blouse. David stood in the doorway, the heat of anger coming off his skin, his blue eyes sultry and flicking with lights. 'You're not really going, are you, Melanie?'

'I thought I told you last night. Yes, David.'

'I thought you'd sleep on it and refuse.'

'Why ever would I do that?' She turned away from him, very slight and graceful in her neat pants and shirt, picked up her brush and ran it through her long hair. She would have to tie it back so it wouldn't blow in her face.

'Because I *want* you to!' said David. He followed her into the room and pushed the door shut, his face dangerous. 'Nothing is the same between us, is it?'

She halted, the brush arrested in mid-air. 'You too

156

are different!' she defended. 'You're not the same easy, contented person you were in London.'

'Nothing mysterious about that. I was on holiday. I tend to relax away from my family, but I still love you, Melanie, more than ever—and I'm tired of getting the brush-off.'

'But we've seen a great deal of each other, David. What more do you want?'

'Don't make excuses!' he snapped.

'I'll have to this once. I haven't had breakfast and Jay would want me to be punctual.'

'Oh yes, we've all got to jump when Jay cracks the whip!' A fresh anger jetted into David's face. 'You're not going anywhere. Jay's not back yet anyway. He's always come between me and what I want.'

'I don't think you're fair to him!' Melanie murmured half hopelessly.

'And how have you formed that conclusion? I mean, you've only been here a short time.'

'I don't want to quarrel with you, David!' she said steadily.

'You don't want anything of me!' he hurled at her bitterly.

'And I detest scenes!'

'How bloody British!' He moved nearer her with a peculiar triumph. 'Put that hairbrush down. You haven't got the guts to tell me you don't love me. My God, what an appalling mistake you've made, but you're going to live with it. I want you just the same.'

She shuddered, losing all her colour, her beautiful eyes fixed on him with compassion. 'The very last thing I wanted was to hurt you,' she said quietly.

'Then there's no harm in letting me hold you.' He reached for her and she didn't try to evade him. His mouth was consuming, but it couldn't wipe out the vision of Jay. She didn't love David, she never had loved him. She was convinced of it. All she felt was a violation but she had to accept a large part of the blame. She was culpable—but surely not entirely? Even if she had never met Jay, David in all his dimensions was a revelation. There could never be any happiness for her with him.

His mouth burned her eyes and her temples, his hands hurting her. 'Lord, how I love you! Please don't go with Jay. Scrub him off.'

'You're hurting me, David! I must go, I promised!'

'Damn it, that's not what's driving it!' He cupped her chin holding her face close.

'You're so possessive!' she complained.

'I thought women liked it.'

'In reasonable doses, perhaps.'

'You should have warned me you were frigid,' he said cuttingly.

'Am I? You don't sound too sure!'

His fingers bit into her. 'I could change it, if you'd let me. Why are you keeping me from you like this? It's a compliment, isn't it, to want a woman? You're so beautiful. You're at your loveliest here, do you know? And you promised to marry me.'

'I *didn't*, David!'

His eyes swept over her, not bothering to hide the desire he felt for her. 'You did!'

'I thought I loved you!' she said sadly.

'Thought?' He drew back from her then, his eyes

158

terrible. With a pounding heart Melanie knew he was going to strike her and involuntarily she flinched. It was no use—David caught the side of her face sharply with the palm of his hand. It was like a dream and he was ranting on in a low voice. Her head was ringing and she couldn't hear him. She put up a hand to her burning cheek at the same time that he drew back.

'You know now, I'll have nothing further to do with you.'

'Do forgive me!' he jeered, 'but you're the guilty one. You know what you are?'

'I know you're ugly and I know I've hurt you and I'm sorry for that, but I won't be punished for not loving you. You're not actually all that lovable. I made a mistake.'

'There *was* no mistake!' he whispered fanatically. 'You're here and you're going to marry me. Why else did I send you that ticket. *One* way, sweetheart, don't forget it!'

Melanie studied him gravely. 'You oppress me, David. You're such a contradiction, and it goes back a long time before you ever met me. I'd like to help you, but I can't!'

'Believe me, I'll make you happy!' he said passionately.

'While I go in fear of your jealous rages?'

'What did you expect, *perfection*?'

'You fall far short of that,' Melanie said quietly. 'I had an image of you that has quite gone away.'

He made an effort to speak naturally, not looking at the marks of his fingers on her cheek. 'I couldn't bear it, Melanie, if you went away and left me.'

'I'll have to now!' she said, and there was a slight break in her voice. 'I'm here under false pretences and I find it unbearable.'

David looked at her, her silvery beauty that was not for him, jealousy of his brother a religion with him. 'What a fool I've been!' he said harshly. 'It's Jay, isn't it?'

'I'm too sickened to remember.'

'Found your tongue, have you?' He laughed with a flash of cruelty. 'I could crush you until you didn't have a thought of Jay in your head.'

'You'd need help,' she said. 'You're only got one arm and you're not very brave.'

'What happened on Coraki?' he demanded, his blue eyes staring into hers.

She answered steadily, 'Jay accomplished what he set out to—prevent any violence being done to a member of his staff.'

'You've got that off pat, haven't you? Good old Jay! Oh my, yes, he's resourceful beyond imagination. Do you love him? It won't do you any good if you do!'

'I know that!'

'So you do!' He was pinning her back against the hard edge of the bureau.

'What kind of a man are you?' she asked slowly.

He had her locked fast. 'Even so we're getting somewhere.'

'That we are,' Melanie could not help but agree. Things were being forced out into the open—things she would rather hide.

It was Hilary who saved her, speaking up boldly on the other side of the door. 'What's going on in there,

160

Dave? You're shouting so we can hear you all over the house!'

Melanie slid out of Dave's grip and went to the door, flinging it open. 'Do come in, Hilary!' she invited.

'Don't worry, I was going to!' Hilary's snapping brown eyes took in the situation at a glance.

Dave looked at her with repugnance. 'Dear old Hilary! As interfering as she's tall!'

'What a rotten swine you are, Dave,' she said, quite in control of herself.

'It's good to see you too!'

'I take it the romance has ended?' she observed.

'You must be pleased!'

Hilary glanced at the silent Melanie. 'Oh, I am. He's not right for you, Melanie, you must see that?'

'Tell us *please*, do you think you are?' Dave peered.

'You never seemed to mind making love to me once!' Hilary pointed out with a wonderful contempt in her face.

'That was a century ago!'

'Damn you, Dave!' she snapped.

'You're welcome!'

Melanie just looked at them, her face very pale except for the dying imprint of David's fingers. Her heart was fluttering. 'I'm going!' she said quietly.

'Not with Jay you're not!'

'Ah, leave the girl alone!' Hilary burst out in disgust. 'Besides, if you go bothering her, you might find Jay cares a good deal. *He's* a gentleman!'

Dave threw his good arm out violently. 'Jay doesn't care about anyone or anything but the chain!' he said with conviction. 'He's a chip off the old block!'

161

'You really believe that, don't you?' Hilary said with wonder. 'Why, Dave *why*? It couldn't be further from the truth. You've a real paranoia about your brother. I don't know why he doesn't knock you to the ground. He could do it easily enough, and he just might when he sees Melanie's face.'

'Is it so obvious?' Melanie asked, with no desire to look in the mirror.

'Yes,' Hilary said bluntly. 'Why don't you go and splash some cold water over it? I'm really sorry, Melanie. You're a guest in this house, and Dave's behaviour is unforgivable. It shames us all.'

'Splendid, Hilary!' Dave saluted her. 'You'd dream up any angle to separate me from Melanie.'

'You've done that, boyo, not me! And well you know it!'

'What a great day it will be when you never set foot in this house again!' he snarled.

His cruelty shocked Melanie. She fled. Hilary didn't, however. She chose to ignore him, sinking into an armchair, just looking at and through him. After a while Dave sat in the chair opposite her and began to pour out his seething agony of disappointment.

Her heart bursting, Melanie slid from the saddle to the firm sand of the river bank. She stood there for a moment, then moved back to tether the colt to a branch of a tree. It was all over, finished. She walked to the edge of the water, her eyes dazzled by the silver glitter, then she bent down and cupped her hands, filling them with cold, clear water, splashing it over her heated face. probably back at the stables she had whipped up a storm, for it was not the colt that had been saddled up for her but the sweet-tempered mare, Victoria.

Ebony suited her better—a beautiful, well above average pure bred and highly mettled, but Melanie was no novice. She had the ability and understanding to handle him. After an initial buck when she mounted him, she had gained quick control, her hands and her voice sympathetic but authoritative, urging him forward from a trot to a canter until they were clear of the main grounds. After that, she gave him his head. He performed beautifully, stretching powerful slender legs to their fullest extent, with no further sign of temper.

It was recovery of a sort, the jacaranda sky, the limitless flats thickly sown with everlasting daisies, the cool belts of trees, the distant shimmer of gullies and water channels, the ragged purple line of the ranges and westward the great parallel lines of the sand dunes with their rippling wind patterns. Flying against the wind seemed to lessen the agony, a compensation, that deadened the pain and the humiliation of that scene with David. Such a long trek for so little! Yet this life could have been hers for the taking. David still wanted her, but David could be unmerciful. It would never have worked out.

She would write to her father, but she wasn't going home. Not yet. She would get a job in this land of opportunity, pay off her fare and perhaps work her way around the country. And then ... and then ... Her feeling for Jay was so intense she felt the memory of him might rule her for ever. It was so beautiful by the river, shaded with bauhinias, cassias, coolibahs and acacias. The sun glinted on brilliant bird feathers in the colours of the rainbow. A wedge-tailed eagle soared above her, then coasted down-wing and disappeared into the tops of the trees. Reeds and grass fringed the banks and unusual purple lilies that were very fragrant. The peace and quiet was remarkable. Further down-stream, a heron was fishing a hole for yabbies, coming up with a golden perch in its beak. A friendly presence watched this place.

When she was calmer she would go to the house. Per-haps David would apologise, perhaps not. Her refusal to marry him had been a crippling blow to his pride, but he would get over her, in time. She would get over Jay, too. Maybe. She might even emerge with some small knowledge of herself that she had never had before. It had only taken a day for Jay to disrupt her life. No, not even a day—a minute. It seemed to her now that she had been waiting for him all her life. Certainly his personality had engulfed her completely like a revelation. She never knew if he was her dream or reality. Her face softened with tenderness and the physical intensity of love. Such a mystery! And now there would be repercussions, endless repercussions. At least she had her pride, and that was important. How she felt about Jay she could keep to herself, hidden under those infinite layers he had wanted to peel away. For an hour or two she would lie quietly, replenishing her courage and stamina in this wondrous peace, all the quieter for the ceaseless twittering of the birds. She was alive. She had perfect health. It was up to her to fight out of her chains.

The sunlight, filtered by the bush willows, slanted across her bare head. Her hair seemed spun of tiny sequins, the light dancing along the shining strands. The ride and the wind had whipped up colour into her cheeks and her green eyes glowed with emotions so momentous they were not under control. The surface of the water was blindingly brilliant. Melanie lay back on the warm sand and closed her eyes. She had never felt so alone in her life. She wanted to be happy, but such unexpected things happened to prevent it. No sooner did she take one fence than another loomed up. If she had to cry, she would cry silently, inside herself. The storm had broken too soon over her head, but she would have been dishonest to try to hide the truth. She had found very early that her knowledge of David was slight and she had gone beyond hiding it. Now her reason for being on Coorrabin was gone. Jay, who stirred her as no man ever would, had his own life, and David was his brother. Her position was untenable.

The sun was dazzling her shut eyelids as she began to think over her life. What had really led her to this place? Her mother's early, tragic death, her adolescent unhappiness? Sybil with her own little derangements had done her best to drive her out of her home. Jealousy was as much a curse as having horns growing out of one's head. She had her work. It was sometimes frenetic, but she enjoyed it and she was very good at it. She had enjoyed her fair share of masculine attention—more than her fair share, according to Jo-Ann whose children's stories she illustrated. Jo-Ann had repeatedly invited her to all sorts of functions and parties. She would have to write to Jo-Ann, and probably Jo-Ann would say: I told you so. Strangely she had not been over-enamoured of David, though like me women she recognised his obvious attractions, his good looks and his charm—and he *did* have it if he was not crossed—his moneyed background.

Melanie gave a little shuddering sigh, bemused by the upsetting events of the morning. She hadn't had breakfast either, not that that was important. One survived these dilemmas, even if one never really recovered. A spent leaf spiralled down on the breeze and glanced off her face. It was beautiful, this green silence, the air smelling of boronia and the purple lilies. There was nothing so soothing as the gentle hand of nature. She wanted to remember nothing, so she turned her head languorously along her bent arm, willing herself weightless, falling, falling, like the spent leaf ...

When she opened her eyes again, Jay was sitting slightly above her on the bank, his head turned away from her looking towards the bend in the river.

'Jay?' she said his name, spellbound, so disoriented for a moment it was difficult to swing into a sitting position.

He turned his head. His face looked carved out of teak, his eyes so glittery she gave an involuntary shiver. 'I'm sorry I couldn't wait for you,' she said.

A muscle jerked beside his mouth. He looked as if he was holding himself on a tight rein, his luminous eyes at variance with the dark formidability of his face. 'How are you?' he asked, quick and hard.

'All in one piece!'

'You look like a tormented child!'

'I'm *all right*, Jay!' she snapped.

'Well, I'm damned well not! I was none too gentle

166

with Dave either.' He spoke emphatically, the anger still in his face.

'I never wanted to cause trouble,' said Melanie miserably.

'Well, you have!'

Colour rushed up under her skin and she shook her head. 'Anyone can make a mistake.'

'Don't I know it!' His brilliant eyes were trained on her, almost piercing the skin with their icy intensity.

'Then why are you so angry?' she asked.

'I'm not angry with you, Melanie,' he said bluntly. 'I'm angry with Dave.'

'Then forgive him. I've hurt him badly.'

'You've done that.'

'I couldn't marry him when I don't love him!' she said, her lovely face clouded with pain.

'My dear Melanie, I never considered it for a minute!'

Such glittery arrogance was chilling her right through to the bone. 'Families stick together, don't they?' she said hardly.

'It's better that way!' he said crisply. 'If it means anything to you, I care about you as well. Dave's problem, or rather the problem of Dave, has to be resolved!'

'Then consider it carefully. Forget about me. I'm a perfect idiot. I've come all this way ...'

'Oh, stop that!' He picked up a stone and sent it skimming along the surface of the water in a half blind frustration.

'You didn't fight with him, did you?' she queried.

167

He glanced at her briefly. 'Be in no doubt about that. I told him to get out.'

'Oh, how deep a hole can I dig for myself!' she said, lightheaded with wretchedness.

'I'd find you unerringly. Things are a little complicated at the moment, but we'll get out of it.'

'What did David say?' She twisted her blonde head to him, wrapped up in her misery.

'I gather he wishes to please me now. I've been too lenient in the past. A great thundering knock about improves Dave no end.'

'It's not David who has to go!' she said emotionally. 'I do.'

'But you've just arrived.' The anger seemed to have died out of his voice.

'Well, I shouldn't like to stay any longer.'

'What do you want to do, Miss Kent?' asked Jay.

'See Australia now I'm here. Get a job. Pay back my fare.'

'Who wants it?' he said with weary patience.

'David might!'

He looked at her, her face buried in her arms. 'I don't like to see you suffer unduly, little one. Your fare was taken care of by the station. Think no more about it.'

'That's not the point!' she burst out.

'I don't think I want to hear what that is.' He looked down at her with hard determination. 'Show me your face.'

'There's nothing wrong with it!' Melanie moved her shoulders fretfully.

'Let me decide that!' In his usual decisive, high-handed way he tipped her face back over his arm.

'Who told you anyway?' she asked faintly. 'Hilary?'

Jay let go of her abruptly. 'Don't be surprised. Hilary is a beggar for punishment. Dave means a lot to her, for some reason that escapes me at the moment. Hilary will be there to pick up all the pieces. She's not one for inaction.'

'And she knows him rather well—something I never did.'

'My poor little girl, you scarcely had the time,' he said softly.

'I suppose there are far more important things than a mere physical attraction,' she admitted 'and that's all David felt for me.'

He gave a hard laugh. 'I'm not sure you understand your own appeal. You'd confuse any man.'

'Not you, Jay!'

'You're slowing me up!' he said with his first show of amusement.

'Women are pawns to MacCallister,' she shrugged.

'I sometimes think we'd be better off without them.' She looked up at him, an odd pleading in her eyes. 'I want to leave, Jay, as soon as possible.'

'I'd be the last man in the world to hold you against your will.'

Some note in his voice made her spring to her feet like a doe. The words tumbled out, defensively. 'What it adds up to is this. You have to accept my decision and help me. I'm told you're a man of considerable heart!'

'That might make it difficult for me to send you away.'

'I *want* to go, Jay!' she pleaded.

'So you believe in burying yourself in the business world?'

'Yes!' she said, her voice sharp with panic.

'Do you think it will work?'

'Nothing is working here!' she said wildly. 'The situation is right out of hand.'

'Maybe you deserve it, the way you turn men's heads!' He got to his feet in one lithe movement, so tall and wide-shouldered she fell back a few paces, almost swaying on her feet.

'Be quite sure I don't want to turn yours!' she said, colouring.

'Who knows, perhaps you have!'

'Then it was an accident.'

'I see.' Jay looked at her small tense face, the young girl fright she was displaying. 'All right, Melanie, I suppose there are worse things than letting you flutter your wings. See a bit of Adelaide—you'll love it. I have relations all over the countryside, but our best bet would be Aunt Kate. She's my mother's only sister. She lives by herself in a lovely old house in the Adelaide hills. It's much too big for her now Uncle Luke is dead and the family are all married and settled elsewhere, but she won't sell it. Katy would love to have you—you're just the right type. You bear a superficial resemblance to both my mother and Katy when they were girls. She'll very likely spoil you, and you can do with a bit of that.'

'I don't think I could impose on her, Jay!' said Melanie, looking down at her hands.

'She's very respectable!' he said dryly.

'Speak sensibly!' she implored him, her eyes iridescent in her small face.

'I am sensible. *You're* the little idiot!'

'I guess I am!' Her delicate shoulders slumped. 'What will you tell her?'

'Leave it to me.'

'I suppose I have to,' she sighed.

'Who else have you got?' Jay asked reasonably.

'I had David!' she said with regret for the might-have-been.

'And you've still got him if you want him. Don't underrate the depth of his feeling.'

'But I don't *love* him, Jay. I'm very sorry.'

He looked exasperated with all this sad passion. 'Don't think you have to lash yourself on Dave's account. No one yet has discovered the secret of loving to order. Maybe you're the first big setback Dave's ever had in his life, but he'll get over it. It may even do him some good.'

'He lost his mother and he adored her!' she cried perversely.

'*He* adored her, my God!' His silver glance slanted over her unpleasantly. 'What about me?'

'But you're strong, Jay, you don't need anybody!'

'Don't I?' Her opinion seemed too much, like a lick of flame towards dynamite. 'How much of this do you you think I can take?'

A soft shiver ran through her. She felt helpless, suspended in some dark fantasy, craving and dreading what was surely going to happen. She looked so enslaved, so fascinated, her green eyes staring at h that Jay reached for her with a hard compulsion and pulled her into his arms.

'You damned well know I want you!'

'Yes, and I'm glad! You can do with a set-down as well!'

'But it won't be from you, Melanie!' he said softly. 'If you think that, you're vastly mistaken!'

'That's only your theory, Jay MacCallister. I'm glad, and I'm going!'

'What terrible manners you've got!' He looked down at her immobile for a minute, then he threaded his hand through her hair, holding her head hard against the palm of his hand. 'It isn't enough to say goodbye, Melanie. I want something to remember!'

'Haven't I got trouble enough?'

'You're damned right! I'm the wrong man to cross.'

It was like a dream sequence, but she was not irretrievably lost. She hit at his chest in a frenzy. 'If you're going to kiss me, get it over!'

He looked down at her as if she had gone mad. 'Why, Melanie, I swear I never thought of it!' he said blandly. 'I mean, one emotional crisis after the other. It isn't fair, and you're so fragile, almost crushable!'

She couldn't seem to find words. 'Oh, you're maddening, *maddening*!'

'I'm doing my level best!'

Her body crumpled, then relaxed against him, all the fight going out of her. 'Oh, Jay, why are you such a tease?' Her head had fallen foward and he could hardly hear her. His heart was beating strongly beneath her head and she turned it trance-like, pressing her cheek his shirt. He was the most provoking man in the

172

world, but there was such a flame of vitality about him, she wanted nothing more than to melt. His fingers were moving up and down in the small of her back, soothing her much as one would soothe a baby. Her whole body was yielding, deliciously at peace. He was taking her full weight, acting as a shield against the cruel world. His hands were in her hair now, very gentle, then exploring the nape of her neck.

'Hey, don't go to sleep!' he said in a low, amused voice.

'Why not?' She felt so sweetly drowsy, everything was starting to blot out but Jay and his caressing hands.

'Because I've changed my mind!' he said with hard intensity.

Her upturned face was like a flower, very sweet and very still, her eyes losing their soft bemusement, becoming eloquent under his gaze. She gave a funny, lost little cry, and heard the quick intake of his breath. He bent his head and found her parted mouth with a driving need that demanded fulfilment, seeking and arousing her answering desire so that it soared beyond the need for any other form of communication. Living sensation pulsed around them, hemming them in on all sides, as white-hot and radiant as Coorrabin's incredible sun, the most natural and the most dangerous radiance in all the universe.

As abruptly as his desire for her had come, it now went away. He put her away from him and the flame went out. Melanie could only stand there in the h circle of his arm, marvelling. With one of his light transitions he was almost a brother—a kind br certainly, but immensely arrogant, deciding her

Instant help was needed, and there was this trip to Adelaide. People Katy knew in the art world would be sure to help her. All sorts of things be arranged to ensure that she would never be idle. Jay's dynamism left her tonguetied.

She walked back up the bank with him like a spent and obedient child, only too willing to have him arrange her life. At least in Adelaide she would never know such blinding frustration!

CHAPTER NINE

THE phone rang and Katy took the call on the upstairs, bedroom extension. Melanie had gone out for the evening to a private art showing and Katy had decided on an early night. It was probably Helen, her daughter-in-law, and she sighed a little wearily. Helen was a lot of admirable things and requests were always reasonable, but even after twelve years, Katy was never certain if she was being asked or told and treason to refuse. The last request had been the use of the house for one of Helen's very big morning tea parties. Since Richard had won the seat for Melbury, Helen had become an indefatigable political hostess with great plans for the future. At any rate, she was a great help to Richard, who more urgent things to do than drink tea. There nothing wrong with Helen, it was just that she was an *attacking* person, and Katy felt a little tired to a bombardment. Perhaps it was the children to mind, in which case she could accept with pleasure. One of them, Justin, was the image of Luke, and Sarah left them all breathless.

Katy padded over from the en suite bathroom and picked up the phone, trying to infuse some life into her voice.

'Katharine Gardiner here!'

'Sounds more like Catherine the Great!'

'Jason darling!' Katy collapsed on to the side of the bed with unfeigned delight.

'Only two people have ever called me that,' he told her, 'you and mother.'

'My darling boy, where are you?' she demanded eagerly.

'At the airport. Can't you hear all the commotion? I've checked in, now I'm coming out.'

'What a mercy you rang me,' she said. 'I was just going to bed.'

'At nine o'clock?' he asked simply.

'Melanie's out for the evening and we were at the ballet last night, so I thought I'd read a little and catch my beauty sleep.'

'Well, rouse yourself, Katy, on my behalf. One of the things I admire about you most is your adaptability.'

'Oh, I'm adaptable all right!' She laughed into the phone 'I thought it was Helen!'

'You *were* in luck!' he said dryly.

'She's a fine girl, but ...'

'Yes, I know!' he agreed tolerantly. 'I'm declinin have her out again at Coorrabin, however. Rick ar kids, yes. Helen *no*!'

'It wouldn't be easy to keep her out of it,' Katy said dryly.

'We'll face that when it comes. Now, Katy, we're discussing my imminent arrival. Get cracking!'

'Yes, I will, dear, and how nice! I don't feel in the least bit tired now.'

'See you, then!' he said briefly, about to hang up.

'Oh, Jason?' Katy called him back.

'Yes, Katy?'

'Have you eaten? Shall I get you something?'

'Excellent. Something for both of us. Open a bottle as well. I'll be with you in forty minutes if I can get a cab. The place is crowded!'

'Oh, you will, dear, if nobody else can!' Katy said with great faith in him, supported by a lifetime of results.

Jay hung up on her, laughing, and Katy replaced the receiver, smiling as well. Jason was her great favourite. He was definitely a MacCallister, but she could see flashes of Anne in him from time to time. It honestly puzzled her, but she derived more pleasure from his company than that of her own two sons. It didn't seem logical, but at least it was honest. Richard and Eric, strange as it seemed to her, had almost been made over by their wives. She loved them dearly, of course, and was proud of them, but they didn't make her feel alive and happy, an individual, attractive woman, like Jason, and no use to deny it.

With some purpose now, Katy slid the louvred wardrobe door along and pulled out her most gorgeous coat. She always looked nice for her nephew. Although he was Anne's representative, and Katy knew well how much Jason had loved his mother. In many ways he had had a hard life. So much had always been expected of him. What a mercy he had all the qualities his father had demanded. A lesser man might have cracked under the strain. Jake had been a perfectionist with his eldest son, very exacting, with a far more relaxed attitude to his other children, and Susan he had positively spoiled.

The thought of Dave and Hilary crossed Katy's mind and she frowned before preparing to dismiss it from her mind. David had always been his own worst enemy. If he didn't love Hilary exactly, he certainly needed her. Lots of people married on the rebound without courting disaster. In fact Katy had the shrewd suspicion that the marriage would work. She hoped so, for she was fond of both of them and had given them a magnificent wedding present even if they skipped inviting her to the wedding.

Susan and Derryn had been the only ones accorded that privilege, upsetting the Lyall-Watsons as much as it did the MacCallisters. It wasn't out of keeping with David's character. He liked punishing others as much as he liked punishing himself. He wasn't Anne's child any more than he was Jake's. He was himself, and Katy prayed often that he would settle and fulfil his potential. The heart of the matter was that he had grown up in the shadow of his father, then his brother, and he hadn't the temperament or the balance to adjust to it. Hilary was strong and very matter-of-fact and she wanted David on any terms, with no apologies to any one. David wanted a firm hand, a woman he could rule. Helen had received a postcard from Gre dashed off in Hilary's confident hand. It sounded happy —not tremendously happy, but getting along well enough. That was the price Hilary had to pay, and she had accepted it. David, in his sullen moods, flickered through Katy's mind and resolutely she shut him out. David had acted the overgrown schoolboy long enough. Nobody could deny that he was able and handsome. When they came back from Europe let him prove his ability in whatever way he liked. Right now he wasn't popular with his family or in-laws.

The house gown swished around her gracefully. Katy, in her late fifties, was still a very pretty woman, due for the most part to heredity, and a good deal of effort as well, involving diet and exercise and nightly beauty rituals. In her youth, she and her sister Anne had been considered miracles of beauty, and Katy liked to keep the flag flying even if it got harder and harder every year and some days well-nigh impossible. She applied a light touch of make-up and touched up her abundant fair hair that she wore in various smooth knots because long hair suited her best, then she went down to the kitchen and stared hopefully in the refrigerator, and from there to the cellar, hunting up a '63 Coonawarra Cabernet, the first vintage of a most beautiful dry red.

What a pity Melanie had to be out! Cooking was really Melanie's line and Kate had been only too pleased to surrender to her pride of place in the kitchen. Melanie did the marketing as well. She was extremely fficient for such a fragile little thing, with a sweet nerous nature to match her lovely face. Kate had ome very fond of her. The mother of sons, she had come to realise the uniqueness of a daughter's companionship, and Melanie in a few short months had become almost that. She was a dear girl, charming and clever with a pretty wit, an endearing child. Katy, an incurable romantic, had high hopes for her.

David's sudden marriage had upset her dreadfully. It was then that Katy had begun taking her out in earnest, coming out of the retirement she had imposed on herself after Luke's death. At first it had been for Melanie's benefit, then increasingly she began to regain the lightheartedness she thought had died with her husband. It was almost like taking on a new lease of life and at the same time introducing Melanie to a wide circle of friends, one of whom had quickly found her a job with his publishing firm. After that, Melanie could have asked for the moon and got it, being held in idolatry by Ian Barrett, the architect who had taken her out tonight. Melanie liked him and they had a good deal in common, but Katy with her keen perceptions knew exactly where Melanie's heart lay.

Katy awaited Jason's arrival with great pleasure. It was almost four months to the day since he had brought Melanie into her care.

When Melanie arrived home, every light in the house seemed to be burning. She allowed Ian to accompany her to the front door while she said her goodnights prettily, promising to ring him about having lunch one day during the week, then she let herself inside, her smooth forehead pleating. Katy had indicated very plainly she intended having an early night. In fact, she had been running her bath when Melanie left.

'Katy?' she called, glancing around her swiftly. All lit up the house was really beautiful, gracious and welcoming.

'In here, dear! I've a visitor.'

Melanie didn't have a shadow of suspicion. Katy had a very large circle of friends, all of whom seemed to drop in whenever the whim took them and largely unannounced. She followed the direction of Katy's voice, dropping her evening purse and the sea green chiffon cape that went with her dress on the Regency cabinet in the hallway.

'How was the evening?' Kate called.

'Oh, a great success! Thirty of the paintings were sold. Ian managed to ...' She broke off abruptly, caught into utter stillness, with the flood of light on her, a naiad of startling beauty. *'Jay!'*

'Melanie!' he responded with a sardonic inflection, and walked towards her, in no way shockingly confronted as she was. 'Adelaide suits you!' he pointed out dryly. 'Why didn't you bring Ian in?'

'He wanted to, but I ...'

'I don't wonder!' he cut in smoothly, bending his dark head swift as a hawk and touching her cheek with his mouth. 'Don't look like that, Melanie, it's not such a surprise, is it?'

'Yes, it is. I'm sorry!' Her eyes were huge, and her hair was a living aura about her flushed face. She spun around, her long skirt swirling about her feet like sea foam. 'Couldn't you have warned me, Katy?'

Katy spread her hands, laughing. 'Jason was against it, dear. We've had such a lovely time!'

'Yes, I can see that!' Miraculously Katy looked ten

180

years younger, beckoning Melanie over to sit beside her on the velvet-upholstered sofa. 'We were waiting up for you,' she added.

'How nice!' Melanie said with a kind of reckless gaiety, tilting her head to Jay.

'I believe you've been seeing Barrett for the best part of six weeks,' he said pleasantly.

'You did tell me to flutter my wings.'

'So I did. I didn't expect to be followed so closely, however!'

Katy looked fondly from one to the other. 'Oh, she's in great demand! I find it hard to keep her home.'

'And what were your plans for tomorrow night?' he asked Melanie, his silvery gaze explicit.

'Oh, nothing in particular! Six out of seven nights in the week are sufficient.'

'Sheer bravado, Jason!' Katy said, smiling. 'We're home at least three!'

'Well, it was good while it lasted,' Jay said obscurely.

Katy hesitated for a moment, then she patted Melanie's hands. 'All things considered it's been quite a night. I'm for bed!' She put out her hand and Jay drew her to her feet.

'And thank you, you blessed woman, for the pleasure of your company. I won't say a word about the burned dinner.'

'The trouble is, darling,' explained Katy, 'Melanie is the marvel in that department. It wasn't that bad, was it? Luke always said he didn't give a damn if I could cook or not.'

'He was quite sensible of all your other distinctions. No, of course it wasn't bad, it was an occasion!'

'Thank you, dear!' Katy reached up and patted Jay's face and he turned her hand to his mouth.

'Goodnight, Katy. Sleep well!'

'Goodnight, Katy!' Melanie repeated almost breathlessly after him.

'I'm glad you enjoyed yourself, dear. You look lovely, really lovely. I'm sure you could be a celebrity if you tried!'

'A legend, anyway!' said Jay, putting a strong touch of mockery into it.

'Don't keep her up too late, Jason,' Katy ordered, smiling.

'Tomorrow's Sunday, isn't it?'

'Oh yes, I quite forgot. In that case, I shall expect breakfast in bed.'

'I'm sure Melanie will get it, won't you, Melanie?'

'If that's what Katy wants,' said Melanie colourlessly.

'I'm fooling, dear!' Katy smiled over her shoulder. 'Now goodnight. Turn off all the lights, won't you, darling?'

'I might do that now!' said Jay in a brisk tone, following Katy and waiting for her to mount the staircase before he turned off the hall light, the light on the porch, and the big crystal and bronze chandelier in the dining room.

'No sense in running up big bills,' he observed, as he came back into the living room.

'I didn't know you were so economy-minded, Jay!' Melanie was appalled by the way her heart was thumping.

'Just another surprise I didn't tell you about!'

'I'm amazed!'

'It pleases me to surprise you. It breaks down a few barriers!'

She was shaken by the sight of him, the swift arrogant charm of his smile. His image had possessed her mind all these long months and it was very difficult not to respond to his living presence. His voice seemed to be flicking at her in odd little lashes, whipping up all the old excitement. 'And then what?' she asked with a soft little lilt.

'Attack.'

'Really, it sounds terrible!'

'Of course if you'd rather go to bed——?' he suggested.

'I really have been out most nights this week,' she assured him.

'You don't look tired, so why run away?'

'I'm not running!' she said, meeting his eyes for an interminable minute.

'Good. There's ten thousand questions I want to ask you but not a one of them springs to mind.'

'I've missed you,' she said.

His silver eyes sparkled, there was a faint smile on his mouth. 'Yes, and it doesn't get better with practice!'

'Heard from David?' she asked.

Jay shook his head, glancing at her rather searchingly. 'I didn't expect it. Sue's heard, of course. Katy had a few postcards and Hilary rang her parents from Paris. They'll be away eight or nine months in all, enough time for Dave to settle down.'

'More importantly, for David to be happy,' said Melanie.

'Well, it won't be for the want of trying. A trip around the world doesn't strike me as a penance.'

'He does love Hilary, doesn't he?' Her green eyes pleaded with him to confirm it.

'Let it rest!' he said briefly. 'Hilary and Dave understand one another.'

'That usually leads to love.'

'Amen.'

'Don't make it sound so cynical!' she begged.

'Who, me?' he smiled at her carelessly, 'I'm a romantic!'

'You mean you're a ...'

'*Please*, Melanie!' he said, sounding shocked. 'You seem curiously intent on those flowers. In a minute I suppose you'll start tearing them apart, scattering the petals all over Katy's carpet. He loves me. He loves me not!'

'I'm trying to clear my mind!' she said, her voice guarded.

In the soft lighting his skin was dark copper. His leather jacket was slung carelessly over the arm of a chair, and his checked black cotton shirt had the same stripe in it as his camel-coloured slacks. He looked casual but very elegant with his tall, lean frame, and it occurred to her with no surprise that he looked good in anything, an old bush shirt and jeans, the beautiful Italian shirts he wore in the evenings, or the easy casualness of now, the brass buttons on his shirt pockets glinting discreetly. She leaned forward a little to hear his next maddening words, her eyes luminous.

'Katy's been praising you up to the skies!' he said

with no echo of Katy's regard. 'She's always regretted not having a daughter.'

'She's been very kind to me!' Melanie answered with sincerity. 'I'd like to repay her some way.'

'That's easily done!'

'Tell me?'

'Oh, I think you're quite capable of working it out for yourself. Come here, Melanie.'

'No, I won't!'

'I'd have been disappointed if you hadn't said that. All right, I'll come and get you. I'm good at it, don't you think?'

'You have enough ego for ten men!' she said crossly.

'Isn't there anything to redeem me?'

Yes, I love you, she thought, but said absolutely nothing, pleating her chiffon skirt with her fingers, her heart throbbing with a bitter-sweet anguish. Why was she so reluctant to tell him she loved him? God knows she had longed for him avidly enough. He was the very pulse of life, and she couldn't kill off all this passionate feeling.

Jay was looking at her with a faint smile. 'You're so beautiful, Melanie, I don't think you're real. Are you?'

His voice sounded so relaxed, she was quite unprepared for the swiftness of his actions. He swooped over her and lifted her into his arms, relishing her slightness, before dropping back into an armchair with his unprotesting burden. 'Now perhaps I'll find out!' His fingers were running over her silky-skinned arms, his eyes with such a turbulent brilliance Melanie leaned away from him and hid her head in the crook of his arm.

185

'I've nothing to say,' she whispered.

'How about *I love you, Jay*?'

'I won't say it.'

'Then I'll help you. Turn your face up, Melanie. You're under fire. I haven't come all this way for nothing.' He twisted her head to him, his expression a little taut. 'Surely you've had enough time?'

Her heart leapt forward to change that expression. 'It's incurable, isn't it?' she sighed.

'What is?'

'How I feel about you.'

'Don't you know that's what love is? No, you're not going to shut me out. Keep your eyes open.'

'You might read too much from them,' she protested.

'It seems to me I always have. My special talent.'

'I've wanted you so much!' she said, making her own contribution. There were so many sensations crowding in on her.

'Don't be afraid to tell me how much!' he said, faintly dry.

'Oh, I love you for a number of reasons, but I haven't got time to tell you all of them.' She lifted her arms and linked them about his head, past hiding the truth that her eyes were revealing. Very softly, almost tentatively, she began to kiss him—his cheek, the brown column of his throat, the corner of his mouth, butterfly kisses that still made her delirious. The most perfect sweet tide of familiarity was overtaking her, presaging an ultimate surrender.

'Am I to understand you're going to marry me?' he asked, his voice unbearably gentle.

'Yes, if you want me.'

186

'What a question!' he almost groaned. 'A real sizzler! Will you stop those crazy little kisses! Don't you see I'm here to take you home?'

'Then you know what my answer is.'

'I've known that all along. You exist for me, Melanie!'

'How feudal!' she murmured, still kissing him.

'Yes, isn't it, but do you want to deny it?'

'No. I feel so wildly, incredibly happy!' Totally unaware of what she was doing, she slipped her hand inside his shirt, caressing his skin with the sensitized tips of her fingers. He let her for a moment, watching the lights in the long silky strands of her hair that fell over his sleeve, then he stopped her hand, holding her still.

'I love you, Melanie, and I need you more than anyone in this world.'

'I hope so,' she said wistfully, 'because that's how I feel about you.'

'Simplicity itself!' His voice dropped to a dark murmur and he lowered his head, irresistibly drawn by her soft, waiting mouth. 'Ring your father tomorrow. We'll have him out for the wedding.'

'That means Sybil too.'

'Don't worry about Sybil. I'm good at making women behave. Besides, she'll be thrilled to see you married off. We'll send them a return ticket. *You'll* never escape!'

'It was touch and go for a while!' Melanie reminded him.

His sudden laugh was like a bell in his throat. 'If you believe that, you'll believe anything. I found you profoundly disturbing from the very first moment. Up until then I never approved of love at first sight!'

'Kiss me, Jay!' she said urgently.

'I'm going to, until you scream for help.'

'*Never!* Anyway, Katy's asleep.'

'In that case ...'

Jay bent his head, smiling, but uncannily ardent, preparing to capture a mermaid, but this time he found a woman, ready to reveal the infinite number of ways she loved him.

Did you miss any of these exciting Harlequin Omnibus 3-in-1 volumes?

Anne Hampson

Anne Hampson #3
Heaven Is High (#1570)
Gold Is the Sunrise (#1595)
There Came a Tyrant (#1622)

Essie Summers #6
The House on Gregor's Brae (#1535)
South Island Stowaway (#1564)
A Touch of Magic (#1702)

Margaret Way

Margaret Way #2
Summer Magic (#1571)
Ring of Jade (#1603)
Noonfire (#1687)

Margaret Malcolm

Margaret Malcolm #2
Marriage by Agreement (#1635)
The Faithful Rebel (#1664)
Sunshine on the Mountains (#1699)

Eleanor Farnes

Eleanor Farnes #2
A Castle in Spain (#1584)
The Valley of the Eagles (#1639)
A Serpent in Eden (#1662)

Kay Thorpe
Curtain Call (#1504)
Sawdust Season (#1583)
Olive Island (#1661)

---

18 magnificent Omnibus volumes to choose from:

Betty Neels #3
Tangled Autumn (#1569)
Wish with the Candles (#1593)
Victory for Victoria (#1625)

Violet Winspear

Violet Winspear #5
Raintree Valley (#1555)
Black Douglas (#1580)
The Pagan Island (#1616)

Anne Hampson

Anne Hampson #4
Isle of the Rainbows (#1646)
The Rebel Bride (#1672)
The Plantation Boss (#1678)

Margery Hilton
The Whispering Grove (#1501)
Dear Conquistador (#1610)
Frail Sanctuary (#1670)

Rachel Lindsay

Rachel Lindsay
Love and Lucy Granger (#1614)
Moonlight and Magic (#1648)
A Question of Marriage (#1667)

Jane Arbor

Jane Arbor #2
The Feathered Shaft (#1443)
Wildfire Quest (#1582)
The Flower on the Rock (#1665)

Great value in reading at $2.25 per volume

Joyce Dingwell #3
Red Ginger Blossom (#1633)
Wife to Sim (#1657)
The Pool of Pink Lilies (#1688)

Hilary Wilde
The Golden Maze (#1624)
The Fire of Life (#1642)
The Impossible Dream (#1685)

Flora Kidd
If Love Be Love (#1640)
The Cave of the White Rose (#1663)
The Taming of Lisa (#1684)

Lucy Gillen

Lucy Gillen #2
Sweet Kate (#1649)
A Time Remembered (#1669)
Dangerous Stranger (#1683)

Gloria Bevan

Gloria Bevan
Beyond the Ranges (#1459)
Vineyard in a Valley (#1608)
The Frost and the Fire (#1682)

Jane Donnelly

Jane Donnelly
The Mill in the Meadow (#1592)
A Stranger Came (#1660)
The Long Shadow (#1681)

Complete and mail this coupon today!

Mail coupon to:
Harlequin Books
MPO Box 707
Niagara Falls, N.Y. 14302

In Canada:
Harlequin Books
Stratford, Ont. N5A 6W4

Please send me the volumes indicated below. I am enclosing my check or money order for $2.25 for each volume ordered, plus 35¢ to cover postage and handling.

- ☐ Anne Hampson 3
- ☐ Essie Summers 6
- ☐ Margaret Way 2
- ☐ Margaret Malcolm 2
- ☐ Eleanor Farnes 2
- ☐ Kay Thorpe
- ☐ Betty Neels 3
- ☐ Violet Winspear 5
- ☐ Anne Hampson 4

- ☐ Margery Hilton
- ☐ Rachel Lindsay
- ☐ Jane Arbor 2
- ☐ Joyce Dingwell 3
- ☐ Hilary Wilde
- ☐ Flora Kidd
- ☐ Lucy Gillen 2
- ☐ Gloria Bevan
- ☐ Jane Donnelly

Number of volumes checked _____ @ $2.25 ea.= $ _____

N.Y. and N.J. residents add appropriate sales tax $_____

Postage and handling $ _____ .35

TOTAL $ _____

NAME _____
(please print)

ADDRESS _____

CITY _____

STATE/PROV. _____ ZIP/POSTAL CODE _____

ROM 2111